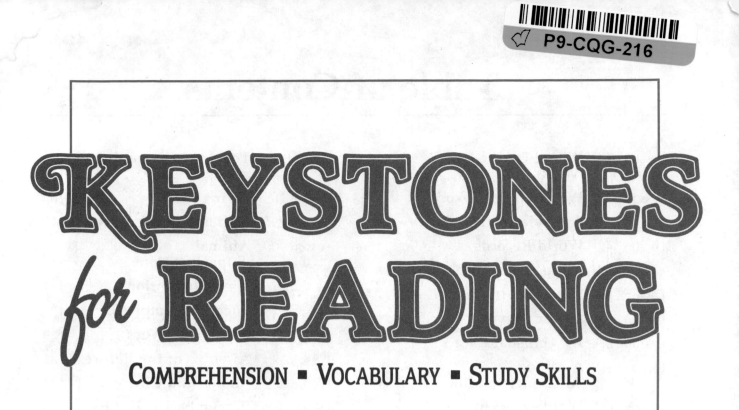

KEYSTONES for READING

COMPREHENSION ▪ VOCABULARY ▪ STUDY SKILLS

Level E

Alden J. Moe, Ph.D.
Lehigh University

Sandra S. Dahl, Ph.D.
University of Wisconsin

Carol J. Hopkins, Ph.D.
Purdue University

John W. Miller, Ph.D.
Georgia Southern College

Elayne Ackerman Moe, M.Ed.
Educational Consultant

MODERN CURRICULUM PRESS
Cleveland ▪ Toronto

Table of Contents

Where Do We Get Words?

Can you think of anything without a name? There's a word for everything, isn't there! Think of all the words you know in the English language. Where did they come from? In this lesson, you'll read about the English language and the *etymology,* or origin, of some words.

---

1 KEYS to Word Origins

English words come from other languages.

LEARN   There are more than 600,000 words in the English language. Nearly eight of every ten words was borrowed from another language.

EXAMPLE   The word *logic* came from the Greek word *logos* which means *word* or *thought.* Logic is good thinking. The word *regret* comes from an old French word meaning *to cry for the dead.* We use the word *regret* when we feel bad about something. *Chauffeur* came from yet another French word which meant *to heat.* Since early cars were driven by steam, the driver had to stoke the furnace that heated the water. The driver then came to be called a chauffeur or stoker.

DIRECTIONS   Write the name of the language from which the root word in each underlined word was borrowed.

1. Mom says she is forever chauffeuring someone.   _____

2. There's surely a logical reason for his behavior.   _____

3. Your answer to this problem is rather illogical.   _____

4. My dad regretted having to miss the game.   _____

Practice With Word Origins

DIRECTIONS Read the word histories and answer the questions below.

Dungaree is the spelling in English of a Hindi word for a coarse cotton cloth, or calico, brought from India.

In old French, the word for *coward* had the meaning "with the tail between the legs." It came from the Latin word for "tail." Most of us have seen a frightened dog put its tail between its legs and slink away.

Sarcasm comes from the Greek word that means "to tear flesh away the way dogs do." Sarcastic words are sometimes spoken of as biting words, for they are intended to bite into the feelings and hurt, as a dog's teeth would hurt flesh.

Parliament comes from a French word *parler* that means "to speak." In Parliament or in Congress, one or another of the members is almost always speaking, usually about a law being considered.

November comes from the Latin word for "nine." November was the ninth month in the ancient Roman year, which began with March.

Nonchalant is borrowed from French and comes from two Latin words meaning "not to be warm." A person who is nonchalant doesn't get warm or passionate about things but seems always to be cool or lukewarm.

1. Which word comes from French and Latin and could describe someone who is calm about most things?

   _____

2. Which language gave English a word for the eleventh month of the year?

   _____

3. Which two languages were called upon for a word used to describe the lion in the movie, "Wizard of Oz"?

   _____

   _____

4. Which French word was borrowed to name an English law-making body?

   _____

5. From which language was a word for "jeans" borrowed?

   _____

6. Which words in the entries have French origins?

   _____

   _____

   _____

Read and Apply

DIRECTIONS Read about how some words found their way into the English language and how some English-speaking people use different words for the same things.

The English language is spoken by more than 450 million people in nearly every part of the world. The more than 600,000 word vocabulary of the English language is larger than the number of words in any other language.

Many English words come from other languages. The people who settled in what is now Great Britain, or England, came from lands where Greek and Latin were spoken. For this reason, a large number of English words were borrowed from Latin or Greek words. The spellings of the English words often differed, however.

Languages other than Greek and Latin have loaned words to the English language. For example, *chimpanzee* and *tote* come from Africa. *Garage, target* and *fashion* are from the French. *Kimono* and *sukiyaki* are borrowed

Japanese words. *Bronco, canyon, cafeteria* and *tornado* were Spanish words, and *kindergarten, hamburger,* and *delicatessen* came to English from the German language.

Still more languages have contributed to the English language. *Algebra* and *magazine* are Arabic words commonly used by English speaking people. *Chop suey, typhoon,* and *won ton* are from the Chinese language, while *tapioca* and *vanilla* come from the Mexican people. *Molasses* and *tank* were Portuguese words, and *pepperoni, balcony, pizza, macaroni,* and *spaghetti* were Italian words.

When North America was first explored, the people had no words for animals and plants they'd never seen before. Naturally, each new thing needed a name. The hickory tree was named by the Native American Indians from the word *pawchoiccora*. The moose, coyote, hummingbird, bullfrog, chipmunk, raccoon, and many other new sights were also named by the Native Americans.

Spanish explorers used the word *mesa* to name the flat-topped mountains they encountered, while the word *prairie* seemed appropriate to the French when they first glimpsed the large areas of flat treeless lands in North America.

Although English is spoken far and wide, not all people use the same words to mean the same things. British people, for example, use the word *lorry* to name what people who speak American English call a *truck*. A car's trunk and hood are referred to in England as a *boot* and *bonnet*.

In Australian English, a *friend* would be your *cobber* and a true friend would be your *fair dinkum cobber*. A pair of *sneakers* is called *sand shoes,* and a small *convenient store* is a *milk bar*. You'd "queue up to go into a footy game" which, in American English, would be said, "line up for a football game." Australians write with a *Biro,* which is a pen, run a *message* rather than an errand, and have a *loo* rather than a bathroom.

DIRECTIONS Use what you've learned in this lesson to write the origin of each word.

1. canyons _____

2. sarcastic _____

3. fashionable _____

4. deli _____

5. kindergartener _____

6. totes _____

7. parliamentary _____

8. algebraic _____

9. typhoon _____

10. coyotes _____

11. regretfulness _____

12. hickory _____

13. mesa _____

14. balconies _____

15. magazines _____

16. nonchalantly _____

17. garages _____

18. dungarees _____

19. target _____

20. cowardice _____

21. logically _____

22. November _____

REMEMBER The roots of many English words come from other languages.

Words, Words, Words

Why do we call a filler between two slices of bread a *sandwich?* Where did we get the word *quiz?* In this lesson, you'll learn about the etymology, or origin, of many words which have been added to the English language.

1 KEYS to Word Origins

Words are added to the English language in different ways.

LEARN New English words have been formed by shortening, abbreviating, or combining other words. Another source of new words is the acronym, a word formed from the first letters of one or several words.

EXAMPLE *Mr.* Cole watched *TV* while eating a *BLT*. He saw an *ad* for a *bike* he might order *COD*.

The words *Mr., TV, ad,* and *bike* are shortened forms of *Mister, television, advertisement,* and *bicycle. COD* and *BLT* are acronyms for *cash on delivery* and *bacon, lettuce, tomato.*

DIRECTIONS Write each underlined word in the correct column below to tell its source.

1. Mrs. Malloy sent her tax return to the IRS.
2. The phone I ordered was postmarked Dec. 6.
3. My grandfather works in the lab at NASA.

acronyms	combined words	shortened words	abbreviations
1. _____	1. _____	1. _____	1. _____
2. _____	2. _____	2. _____	2. _____

2 Practice With Word Origins

DIRECTIONS Words have been added to the English language when new ideas, products or services are invented, or when a word is needed for a sound that people hear. Read each sentence and think about a word you know that was created for each need. Write the word on the line.

1. People wanted to talk about the sound a cow made.

_____

2. A new kind of engine was invented by Rudolf Diesel.

_____

3. People looked for hotels along the way as they motored across the country.

_____

4. A duck diving into water made an interesting sound.

_____

5. A word was needed to mean any information put into a computer.

_____

6. A product, invented to quickly close a jacket, skirt, or pants, made a unique sound.

_____

7. A part on cars that cushioned any bumps needed a name.

_____

8. A process for sterilizing milk was discovered by Louis Pasteur.

_____

DIRECTIONS Write *shortened, invention, abbreviation, sound imitation, combined,* or *acronym* on the line to tell the origin of each underlined word.

1. Jake escorted the <u>VIP</u> all over town in the <u>limo.</u>

   VIP _____

   limo _____

2. Mona <u>sighed</u> when she got her <u>Salk</u> vaccine.

   sighed _____

   Salk _____

3. Chuck and Nancy often work <u>overtime</u> as <u>FBI</u> agents.

   overtime _____

   FBI _____

4. Dr. Wallace gave an <u>outstanding</u> talk last night.

   <u>Dr.</u> _____

   outstanding _____

Read and Apply

DIRECTIONS Read about the etymology of more words in the English language.

Some words have interesting stories behind their origins. For example, the word *quiz* started as a joke. In 1780, the manager of a theater in Dublin, Ireland bet that he could create a new English word. He then wrote "q u i z"—at that time four meaningless letters—on walls throughout Dublin. People began to realize it was a joke and *quiz* took on the meaning of "trick" or "puzzle" and later, "test."

New words are often named for the people who were instrumental in a new activity or development. Often the person is long forgotten, though the word becomes common. In the early 1800's, Captain Charles Boycott was so unfair with people in Ireland who rented land from his employer, that the renters decided they would cease speaking to him and his family.

People still boycott when they believe an employer is unfair.

The sandwich was invented in 1762 by a man who did not want to take time to eat. John Montague, the English Earl of Sandwich, liked to play cards. During one long card playing session he had beef and slices of bread brought to his table. Others also began to take up this new way of eating and, thus, the sandwich became popular.

Then there were words which you may never have thought were acronyms. If you've ever used underwater breathing equipment, you know the word *scuba*. *Scuba* is an acronym for each of the first letters of <u>S</u>elf-<u>Con</u>tained <u>U</u>nderwater <u>B</u>reathing <u>A</u>pparatus. *Radar* is an acronym for <u>ra</u>dio <u>d</u>etecting <u>a</u>nd <u>r</u>anging.

Speaking of words, you've probably heard your share of bunk from those who talk constantly and don't say anything of importance. The word *bunk* was first used in 1819 to describe the endless and boring speeches of Felix Walker who was a representative to the United States Congress from Buncombe County, North Carolina.

Then there was an English physician, Dr. J. H. Salisbury, who thought that beef would be more nutritious if it were ground and mixed with seasonings before being broiled or fried. Today, this ground beef is often mixed with eggs and bread crumbs and served with gravy. Some people consider the salisbury steak to be just a fancy name for a hamburger patty covered with gravy.

Words are interesting. Who knows? Someday you may be responsible for the creation of a new word!

DIRECTIONS Circle the best answer.

1. An example of a word which is, perhaps, used less often than its abbreviation is

   family.   zipper.

   advertisement.   hotel.

2. The study of word origins is called

   etymology.   biology.

   geology.   sociology.

3. Rather than say "United Nations Educational, Scientific, and Cultural Organization," we now say "Unesco." *Unesco* is

   a combined word.   an acronym.

   an invention.   a sound imitation.

4. An example of a word coming from an invention would be

   Adolph Sax's instrument.   honked.

   COD.   backyard.

5. A word that was made by shortening is

   superhighway.   airplane.

   headache.   vet.

6. The words *bark, clop, zap, neigh, honk,* and *cackle* are

   combined words.   abbreviations.

   sound imitations.   acronyms.

7. The word *history* was used to make the word *story.* This is an example of

   a combined word.   a shortened
                                word.

   an acronym.   a sound imitation.

REMEMBER Words come from many sources.

An Aviation Hero

The idea of combining airplanes and medicine was new in the early 1900s. In this lesson, you will learn some new words as you read about air-rescues and the contributions of a true hero.

 ## 1 KEYS to Content Words

Each subject has its own special words.

LEARN Science, social studies, math, health, and other subjects you study have their own special words. In addition, specific topics in each of those subject areas have words that are uniquely theirs.

EXAMPLE You need to know the meanings of two special words to get the most meaning from this sentence you might read in your science or social studies book:

The controller guided the pilot along the tarmac.

Knowing that the word *controller* means one who guides planes to and from airports, and that *tarmac* is another word for runway helps you understand the sentence.

DIRECTIONS Use the words you just learned to complete this paragraph.

Amy's dad works at the airport as a _____.

He often works long hours guiding planes to and from the airport. In the wintertime, the weather conditions can create extra problems. Planes are frequently lined up on the

_____ waiting to depart. Snow and ice on the

_____ create extra work for the ground crews.

DIRECTIONS Read this article about airplanes and aviation. Then use what you read along with the picture to complete the sentences below.

For most people, the fastest way of traveling from place to place is by airplane. Because of the building and flying of airplanes, a large industry, called aviation, has developed. Aviation includes all aspects of flying and its effect on our lives.

The first airplanes carried only the pilot. As airplanes became safer, however, they were built to hold the pilot and one passenger. Most airplanes today carry at least four passengers, with commercial aircraft accommodating as many as 700 people.

1. The main body of an airplane is

   called the _____.

2. An airplane is also called an

   _____.

3. The industry that deals with flying and the operation of airports is

   called _____.

4. The fan-like apparatus on the nose of a plane is the

   _____.

5. _____ airplanes carry hundreds of passengers.

6. Near the end of each wing of an

   airplane is a(n) _____ which is used to turn the plane.

7. The wheels are part of the

   _____ gear of a plane.

8. _____ at the tail of a plane keep the plane level, both horizontally and vertically.

9. The _____ indicate the speed, altitude, and other information about a plane's location when in the air.

10. A plane's _____ is on the vertical stabilizer.

11. A plane's _____ is on the horizontal stabilizer.

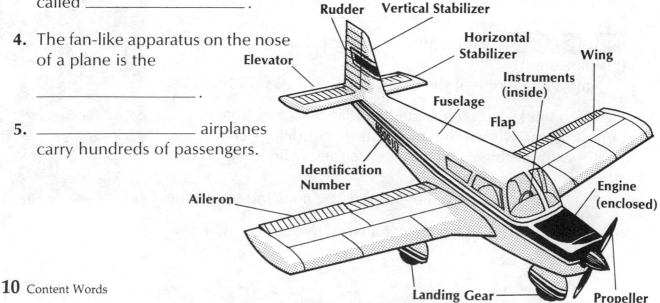

Rudder Vertical Stabilizer Horizontal Stabilizer Wing Elevator Instruments (inside) Fuselage Flap Identification Number Aileron Engine (enclosed) Landing Gear Propeller

3 | Read and Apply

DIRECTIONS Read about an historical figure in the field of aviation.

Marie Marvingt was the third. Only two other women had earned their pilot's licenses before her. Soon after that, Marie gained recognition again by setting a world's record for female pilots. She kept her plane in the air for 53 minutes, during which she traveled a distance of 45 kilometers. Marie loved flying, but she also loved nursing. By combining her interests and talents, Marie Marvingt made heroic contributions in her lifetime.

Disguised as a man during World War I, Marie nursed soldiers, many of whom she rescued from mountaintops with the aid of skis. She also applied her nursing talents for ailing nomads in the Sahara Desert and Eskimos in the Arctic regions. These experiences led Marie to search for a way to more easily transport sick people long or difficult distances.

Marie was convinced that airplanes were the answer. She felt that airplanes could be used not only to rescue people in need of medical attention, but also to assist victims of tornadoes, earthquakes, floods, wars, and other disasters.

As Marie presented her ideas to manufacture ambulance-airplanes to thousands of audiences around the world, she found that some people were reluctant to embrace such an invention. She spent many years gaining the necessary support for her idea. During those years, she trained nurses

in air-rescue work and successfully founded several air-rescue groups.

Marie was honored repeatedly for her undying efforts to help others. She received thirty-four decorations in all, but it was obvious that, to her, none of these was as fulfilling as the joy she realized in knowing that her work benefitted so many people in need.

Read each statement. Use the information from the story you just read to decide if the sentence is true or false. Circle the correct word.

1. Marie Marvingt's efforts led to the design of the ambulance-airplane.   true   false

2. Aviation would include the manufacturing of airplanes.   true   false

3. Marie Marvingt was a woman of many talents.   true   false

4. Marie Marvingt worked during World War II.   true   false

5. An air-rescue group might assist if a ship sank.   true   false

6. Marie Marvingt gave speeches about her ideas only in Europe.   true   false

7. It was common in the early 1900's for a female to earn a pilot's license.   true   false

8. The idea to use aviation to rescue victims was not new in Marie Marvingt's time.   true   false

9. It took little time for the idea of air-rescue to be accepted by people.   true   false

10. Marie Marvingt's efforts led to the use of aviation for the service of humanity.   true   false

DIRECTIONS Use your own knowledge along with the information you've learned about aviation to answer these questions.

1. Why do you think Marie Marvingt was disguised as a man? _____

_____

_____

_____

2. Why do you think some people doubted Marie's idea? _____

_____

_____

_____

REMEMBER Special subjects have special words.

12 Content Words

World Records

Is a smirk the same as a smile? It depends on the precise meaning of the words. Though similar in meaning, a smirk is not exactly a smile. In this lesson, you will learn to choose the best words to express ideas as you read about some special world records.

1 KEYS to Synonyms

Several words can have similar meanings.

LEARN Synonyms are words that mean the same or almost the same. Although no two words have exactly the same meaning, many are very similar. Synonyms allow us to choose the most precise word to describe something.

He put the pencil down.   He slammed the pencil down.

The words *put* and *slammed* give totally different pictures in your mind. A dictionary gives some synonyms. A thesaurus lists synonyms for most common words.

DIRECTIONS Circle one of the synonyms in parentheses that best fits the meaning of the sentence.

1. It is important to (grind/chew) your food before swallowing.

2. The man (tossed/heaved) the paper clip onto the desk.

3. Several pictures were arranged on one of the room's (sides/ walls).

4. Having planned our picnic, we hoped the (climate/ weather) would not change.

5. The chef (peeled/skinned) the potatoes with speed and skill.

Practice With Synonyms

DIRECTIONS Write as many synonyms as you can next to each word. Use a dictionary or thesaurus, if you like.

1. walk _____
2. ate _____
3. break _____
4. run _____
5. laugh _____

6. defeat _____
7. happy _____
8. smart _____
9. pretty _____
10. say _____

DIRECTIONS Use your list of synonyms to replace each underlined word with a synonym. Write the word on the line.

1. The Hawks <u>defeated</u> the Jays 5–0.

_____

2. I love to watch squirrels <u>run</u> around the yard.

_____

3. The couples took a quiet <u>walk</u> through the park.

_____

4. The teacher heard the soft <u>laugh</u> of the two girls in the back of the room.

_____

5. He leaned over the table and <u>ate</u> the food as though he hadn't eaten for weeks.

_____

6. I heard him <u>say</u> it at the top of his lungs!

_____

7. My sister's uniform is <u>pretty</u>.

_____

8. The glass is so fragile, it will <u>break</u>.

_____

9. The fox is renowned for being very <u>smart</u>.

_____

10. We were <u>happy</u> when we won the championship.

_____

Think about words that have the same or similar meanings as you read about some world records.

Have you ever wondered where the world's driest desert is located, or which is its southernmost town? Harry did. For years he had been interested in world records. He could tell you who was the first to swim the English Channel and who had the best career in pitching.

All of these were world records, but Harry realized that they had all been set by people. He began to wonder then about records that were truly "world" records—those set by the world itself. One day he set out to discover those records. He headed straight for the reference book in the library that would help him most, The World Almanac.

Harry found that while the world's largest desert is the Sahara, the driest is the Atacama Desert in Chile. Rainfall there is almost unknown. While the highest spot on earth is Mt. Everest at 29,028 feet, the lowest is the Dead Sea, which is 1,312 feet below sea level. The deepest point in the ocean is the Mariana Trench in the Pacific, nearly seven miles below the surface. The largest lake on earth is the Caspian Sea, which is technically a lake even though it contains salt water. Lake Superior is the largest fresh water lake in terms of area, though Lake Baykal, in the Soviet Union, actually contains more water. It has less surface area but makes up for it in depth. At more than a mile deep, it is the deepest lake anywhere.

Harry was so fascinated by these facts that he decided to do a science report on world records in nature. Needless to say, Harry's report was one of the most interesting the class had ever heard—a real record-breaker!

Locate a similar sentence in the article you just read for each sentence below. Decide which of the words in parentheses is the best synonym for the idea expressed. Circle the word.

1. Have you ever (considered/reasoned) where the world's driest desert is located, or which is its southernmost town?

2. He wondered about records that were truly "world" records—those (arranged/established) by the world itself.

3. He headed straight for the reference (volume/manuscript) in the library that would help him most, the World Almanac.

4. Rainfall there is (nearly/completely) unknown.

5. The southernmost (city/civilization) in the world is Puerto Williams, at the tip of South America.

6. The deepest (place/depression) in the ocean is the Mariana Trench in the Pacific, nearly seven miles below the surface.

7. Lake Superior is the largest fresh water lake in terms of (surface/ size).

8. Lake Baykal, in the Soviet Union, actually (engulfs/has) more water.

DIRECTIONS Use a dictionary to write the definitions to the right of each pair of words. Then explain how the two words differ in meaning. Write a sentence using the two words. The first one is done for you.

1. student/scholar — one who studies/one who excels in studies

   How they differ: Many students are not scholars.

   Sentence: I am a student, but he is a scholar.

2. aroma/odor _____

   How they differ: _____

   Sentence: _____

3. teenager/child _____

   How they differ: _____

   Sentence: _____

REMEMBER Use context to know which synonym best fits the meaning.

Opposites Attract

You're going to the local airport to meet a relative who's flying in to visit. Do you go to the area marked "Arrivals" or "Departures"? In this lesson, you'll learn about words that are opposites as you read about how differently friends may look at things.

KEYS to Antonyms

Antonyms are words with opposite meanings.

LEARN An antonym changes the sentence to its opposite meaning.

The leftover casserole had become *liquid.*
The leftover casserole had become *solid.*

DIRECTIONS Choose an antonym for the underlined word to give each sentence its opposite meaning. Write it on the line.

disclosed	temporary	dismantle
positive	advanced	gruesome

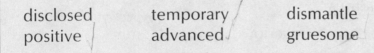

1. This is the <u>negative</u> end of the battery. _____

2. We had a <u>permanent</u> delay in our plans. _____

3. It was a rather <u>picturesque</u> sight. _____

4. He <u>concealed</u> his source of information. _____

5. B.J.'s dog had <u>retreated</u> quickly. _____

6. Will you help me <u>assemble</u> this now? _____

DIRECTIONS Circle the antonym for each underlined word.

1. Sasha's parents painted the <u>interior</u> of their house.

   ceilings   walls   outside   inside

2. Those foods are certainly <u>nutritious</u>.

   unhealthful   tasteless   delicious   undercooked

3. Our neighbor has a <u>gigantic</u> cottonwood tree.

   flowering   huge   dwarflike   gorgeous

4. The leading character in the story was a <u>hero</u>.

   villain   graduate   teenager   robot

5. Mark had that <u>sinking</u> feeling when he finished the test.

   negative   funny   strange   uplifting

6. We'll have to <u>discard</u> some of these papers.

   underline   display   save   correct

7. I <u>withdrew</u> some money at the bank.

   phoned   deposited   loaned   discovered

8. Marcy is <u>unaware</u> about the hazards of riding without a seat belt.

   ignorant   unconcerned   alert   unable

9. Apparently the movie is <u>humorous</u>.

   memorable   amusing   serious   funny

10. We were amazed when we saw the <u>destruction</u>.

    waste   construction   entrance   excitement

11. This is an <u>accurate</u> model of the shuttle.

    incorrect   excellent   ancient   exceptional

12. We went to see the <u>public</u> art exhibit.

    original   delightful   popular   private

Read and Apply

DIRECTIONS Read about how differently two boys look at things.

Chuck and Eddie, though really good friends, were true opposites when it came to how they thought about things. Chuck was what you might call an eternal optimist. He always seemed to look on the brighter side of things. Eddie, on the other hand, took a more negative approach. Whenever anything was planned, it was Eddie who just knew it would go wrong.

"A real pessimist, he is!" thought Chuck as he listened to Eddie claim that their team would never get into the semi-finals, let alone win the championship.

"But Eddie, we've won every game this season and the next best team has only won three-fourths of their games!"

"Be that as it may," scowled Eddie, "something will happen to our luck between now and the semi-finals. I just know it! I'll probably foul out like I always do, and if Matt's not out of his cast by then . . ."

"Hold it, Eddie! You've only fouled out twice this whole season and you know that Matt's supposed to get his cast off tomorrow. The semi-finals aren't for two weeks yet. Think positively for a change! You know, you'd call a half-filled cup half *empty* when you could just as easily say that the cup was half *full!* Lighten up, will you?"

"Yeah, I suppose you're right, Chuck," admitted Eddie, thoughtfully. "I guess that's one of the reasons I like you. You always seem to see the good in everything and everyone. You and I are definitely a good example of that saying about opposites attracting one another! What do you say, let's go out and shoot some baskets. We'll see if your optimism gets you anywhere on the court!"

1. He would not confirm nor deny that he'd done it.
2. Eddie was optimistic, while Chuck was pessimistic.
3. We had a contract until this disagreement.
4. Use the ropes when you ascend as well as descend the mountain.
5. You must keep records of your profits and losses.
6. Eileen was tardy once or twice, but she's usually prompt.
7. I'm not asking you to deny it nor do I want you to confess.
8. What we thought was a major difference turned out to be a minor one.
9. Let's see that our final game goes better than the initial one did.
10. You'll need to insert the card before you can withdraw the money.
11. She promised an approval or denial by Tuesday.
12. They have included you but excluded me.
13. The service department certainly did me a disservice.

DIRECTIONS Use each word from the word box once as you write an antonym for each word below.

normal	agree	disrespectful	formal
obedient	destroy	poverty	beamed
flexible	order	courage	divide
serious	optimism	carefully	bored

1. scowled _____
2. multiply _____
3. excited _____
4. pessimism _____
5. carelessly _____
6. abnormal _____
7. wealth _____
8. salvage _____
9. ridiculous _____
10. riot _____
11. rigid _____
12. naughty _____
13. refuse _____
14. cowardice _____
15. considerate _____
16. unofficial _____

REMEMBER Antonyms have opposite meanings.

Land Down Under

What is the smallest continent that is an island and also a country? In this lesson, you will learn about words that sound alike but are not the same as you read about the land "down under."

1 KEYS to Homonyms

Homonyms sound alike but are different words.

LEARN Words that sound alike but are spelled differently and have different meanings are called homonyms. Reading the whole sentence helps to know which meaning is being used.

EXAMPLE Listen for two words that sound alike as you read this sentence:

Let's pause while Spike licks the snow off his paws.

The words *pause* and *paws* sound alike but have different spellings. *Pause* means to *stop for a moment* and *paws* are the dog's feet.

DIRECTIONS Write the correct word on the line.

1. strait—narrow body of water   straight—not curved

Use your ruler to draw a _____ line.

2. pact—agreement   packed—arranged tightly together

Mia and Char made a _____ to always be friends.

3. roe—a small, graceful deer   row—to move a boat by using oars

Jeff will _____ the boat across the lake.

2 Practice With Homonyms

DIRECTIONS Read each riddle and consider the meanings of the pairs of homonyms. Write the word for the first part of the riddle on line *a* and the second part on line *b*.

ceiling—opposite of floor
oar—a long pole
deer—a fast moving animal
flour—powder made from grains
wring—to twist with force
night—darkness
creak—a squeaking sound
groan—a sound of sorrow
rays—beams of light

sealing—closing completely
ore—a rock or mineral
dear—a term for a loved one
flower—a part of a plant
ring—a thin band
knight—a gallant and brave man
creek—a small stream
grown—fully mature
raise—an increase in wages

1. Wear me on your finger (a) *or* do me when you squeeze hard. (b)

   a. _____

   b. _____

2. I pledged to do good deeds (a) *or* sunset to sunrise. (b)

   a. _____

   b. _____

3. I come from deep in your throat (a) *or* I describe an adult. (b)

   a. _____

   b. _____

4. Fish in me (a) *or* apply oil to make me disappear. (b)

   a. _____

   b. _____

5. I'll help move a boat (a) *or* you can find me in some rocks. (b)

   a. _____

   b. _____

6. I am a swift animal (a) *or* I am much loved and precious. (b)

   a. _____

   b. _____

7. I am ground grain (a) *or* use me as a decoration. (b)

   a. _____

   b. _____

8. Look up at me (a) *or* use me to keep a container airtight. (b)

   a. _____

   b. _____

9. I am an increase in pay (a) *or* light from the sun. (b)

   a. _____

   b. _____

Read and Apply

Look for words that are part of a homonym pair as you read about the land "down under."

Australia is unique in that it is not only a continent and a country, but also an island. It is totally surrounded by the Indian and Pacific Oceans. Australia is appropriately nicknamed "down under," since the whole continent is located south of the equator in the Southern Hemisphere. Another characteristic that makes Australia unique is the unusual animals that live there.

One of the most well-known Australian animals is the kangaroo. There are over forty types of kangaroos, ranging in size from the red kangaroo that stands six feet tall and leaps as far as thirty feet, to the musky rat kangaroo that's a mere six inches in height. The young kangaroo, called a joey, lives inside a pouch on its mother's stomach for the first six months of life. It may venture out, but always returns to eat. When a joey outgrows the pouch, it must then live on its own.

The koala, another of Australia's interesting animals, looks like a teddy bear, although it is not a true bear. Like the kangaroo, koalas are marsupials, which means they carry their young in a pouch. Unlike the kangaroo, however, the koala gets carried on its mother's back when it grows too large for the pouch. It could be said that koalas are dependent on eucalyptus trees for their "room and board," since they spend most of their time in the trees and the eucalyptus leaves are their food. The moisture in the eucalyptus leaves also supplies most of a koala's water supply.

Australia's platypus, with its bill and webbed feet, is one of the strangest animals found anywhere in the world. The platypus has thick fur like an otter and its tail is flat like a beaver's. Female platypuses lay their eggs in a burrow

lined with plants. In about ten days, the eggs hatch, and then some four months later, the young platypuses leave the burrow to take their first swim. The platypus catches small shellfish and insects in the water and stores the food in pouches in its cheeks. It then floats on the surface while eating. The platypus has grinding pads instead of teeth.

These pads are rough and have sharp ridges for chewing.

Since these Australian animals are rare and found only in the land "down under," there are strict laws to prevent their becoming extinct. A flavor of the land "down under" can be had, however, by visiting the various major zoos around the world.

DIRECTIONS Find and circle a word in the article to answer each question. Then write the word on the line.

What is a homonym for:

1. *their* that means "a certain place"?

   _____

2. *Ann* that is called an "article of speech"? _____

3. *read* that means "a color"? _____

4. *fore* that means "in place of"?

   _____

5. *bare* that means "an animal"?

   _____

6. *two* that means "also"? _____

7. *there* that is used to show possession? _____

8. *fir* that means "outer covering of an animal"? _____

9. *tale* that means "the end of"?

   _____

10. *knot* that is used to mean "no"?

    _____

11. *bored* that is made from a tree?

    _____

12. *feat* that is used for walking?

    _____

13. *thyme* that is measured in hours, days, etc.? _____

14. *won* that is a number? _____

15. *bee* that means "to live"? _____

16. *inn* that means "contained by"?

    _____

17. *sum* that means "an amount of"?

    _____

REMEMBER When two words sound alike, check for spelling and meaning.

Soccer Savvy

You have probably never read the words *tsu-chu, episkyros,* or *harpastrum* before. Most likely, you aren't sure how to pronounce them either. In this lesson, you will learn to get the meaning of an unknown word by using the words around it. You'll also gain some soccer savvy.

1 KEYS to Context

Clues around a word can give you its meaning.

LEARN Context is a group of words that go together. When one word in the context is unknown, the other words can help you figure out its meaning.

EXAMPLE Mark reads the other words and makes an *educated guess* when he sees a new word. *Educated guess* means a guess based on all the clues.

DIRECTIONS Use context clues and your own ideas to complete the paragraph. Write one word on each line.

Football and soccer-like activities have been played for centuries. *Tsu-chu, episkyros,* and *harpastrum* are examples of

_____ played in the ancient world. The games

were probably played with a _____ that was

_____ across a playing field similar to football

and soccer fields. Most likely, there were _____

opposing teams. The team with the most _____
won the game, as in team sports today.

Practice With Context

DIRECTIONS Read each sentence and complete the definition.

1. A well-directed pass can *sweep* right past a goalkeeper.

   Sweep means _____

2. To be a good player, an athlete must learn to *propel* a soccer ball with the foot.

   Propel means _____

3. Good kicking demands accuracy and control. It is best to *strike* the ball with the flat areas of the foot.

   Strike means _____

4. A full *swing* of the leg gives the most powerful kick.

   Swing means _____

5. Players pass with the inside of the foot to prevent leg *strain*.

   Strain means _____

6. When properly *executed,* the instep pass results in power and speed.

   Executed means _____

7. In this play, remember to keep your non-kicking leg *wide* to the right or left of the ball.

   Wide means _____

8. As the ball approached, the player *whipped* it into the end zone.

   Whipped means _____

9. A kicker has special problems when his opponents surround him, putting the ball in close *quarters*.

   Quarters means _____

10. A good player keeps his eyes on the ball and *reads* the ball, paying careful attention to its spin, light path, and bounce.

    Reads means _____

Read and Apply

DIRECTIONS Each time you come to an underlined word, gather clues to figure out what the word means.

A good training program in soccer gets team members into condition. In addition, the program teaches the players to work as a cohesive unit. As in any team sport, players working together as a team are more likely to win games.

During practices, the coach evaluates the skills of each player and gives pointers on deficient skills. Then the player practices the skill under the critical eyes of the coach. Practice drills are essential if players are to perfect their skills.

Once the players have built their speed, endurance, strength, and other skills required of team members, the coach schedules a scrimmage. Scrimmages provide an opportunity for players to practice skills in a game-like setting. Coaches supervise each scrimmage carefully. Not only do they try to prevent team injuries, but they also use the game to reinforce soccer rules. Players dress in full uniform to include shin guards which are worn for protection from lower leg injuries.

Once a soccer match begins, the two teams of competitors run at top speed for an hour and a half in fair or foul weather. Each position on the team demands speed, endurance, and strength. Speed is needed during short sprints with the ball as well as for longer runs down the field. Players need endurance and strength to withstand the running and the bruising contact that often takes place in plays near the goal area. Play is roughest around the goal line because the offensive team is trying to get the ball across the goal line, while defensive players do their best to kick the ball upfield.

1. Competitors
   a. coaches
   b. partners
   c. rivals

2. Foul
   a. bad
   b. pleasant
   c. warm

3. Endurance
   a. tiring easily
   b. holding up well
   c. being kind

4. Sprints
   a. long runs
   b. short runs
   c. slow runs

5. Bruising
   a. painful
   b. playful
   c. quick

6. Offensive
   a. trying to score
   b. protecting the goal
   c. being rude

7. Evaluates
   a. practices
   b. praises
   c. judges

8. Deficient
   a. skilled
   b. lacking
   c. learning

9. Perfect
   a. improve
   b. forget
   c. repeat

10. Scrimmage
    a. practice game
    b. line on the field
    c. fight or struggle

11. Supervise
    a. repeat
    b. plan
    c. direct

12. Reinforce
    a. review
    b. replay
    c. weaken

13. Shin guards
    a. head gear
    b. shoulder pads
    c. leg protectors

14. Cohesive
    a. separate
    b. apart
    c. joined together

REMEMBER Use context to make an "educated guess" about a word's meaning.

An Unusual Race

   Would you consider using a bathtub as a race vehicle, or does that sound ridiculous? In this lesson, you'll read about an unusual race as you learn about using all the words you read to help you figure out the meaning of a new word.

1 KEYS to Context

Context is a group of words working together.

LEARN   Using the words around an unfamiliar word helps you guess its meaning. A good way to practice using context is to try to fill in a missing word in a sentence.

   Aaron earned a certificate for his

_____ work.

Several synonyms, or words with similar meanings, could complete this sentence. The words *excellent, good, outstanding, perfect* or any of several other words would make sense and give the sentence the same or similar meaning.

DIRECTIONS Write a word on the line so that each sentence makes sense.

1. The students cut paper with _____ .

2. Climbing mountains can be _____ .

3. A _____ uses electricity.

4. The storm _____ all night long.

5. The noise of the _____ was so loud, it woke me.

6. The first thing the winner bought was a _____ .

② Practice With Context

DIRECTIONS Use the context of each sentence to write the meaning of the underlined word. Then write some synonyms that could be used to give the sentence the same or a similar meaning.

1. Dog racing has been popular since the days of <u>ancient</u> Egypt.

    Ancient means _____

    Synonyms: _____

2. Girls and boys <u>compete</u> in the International Soap Box Derby each year in Akron, Ohio.

    Compete means _____

    Synonyms: _____

3. The English Derby, held near London, is <u>regarded</u> as one of the world's greatest horseracing events.

    Regarded means _____

    Synonyms: _____

4. The world's most <u>renowned</u> sailboat race is the America's Cup race, held every two to four years.

    Renowned means _____

    Synonyms: _____

5. <u>Qualification</u> trials are held each year prior to the Memorial Day Indianapolis 500 Mile auto race.

    Qualification means _____

    Synonyms: _____

6. Bicycle racing is a <u>dominant</u> sport in many European countries.

    Dominant means _____

    Synonyms: _____

Read and Apply

DIRECTIONS Use the context to get the meaning of any unfamiliar words as you read about an odd race in Kansas.

Every year in the month of May, a festival is held in Wichita, Kansas, on the banks of the Arkansas River. Thousands of people flock to the river to see art exhibits, watch hot-air balloons, jog, hike, and listen to concerts. The highlight of the River Festival, however, is a very unusual race. Its participants must traverse 300 yards down the river in bathtubs.

The regulations for the contestants are not complex. First, the entry must include an old-fashioned, cast-iron bathtub. Second, no motors are allowed, although a sail is permitted. Third, no more than two people are allowed to row, pedal, paddle, or otherwise maneuver the "boat" downstream.

Contestants are encouraged to be creative as long as the rules are followed. Their vessels may be embellished with decorations of wood, plastic, cloth, metal, etc. The crafts can be of any size or shape. Some have been made to look like cars, allligators, hamburgers, sailing ships, and other semblances.

On both banks of the river, people recline on the grass and cheer the remarkable crafts onward. Some of the bathtubs move quickly because their designers have utilized tremendous ingenuity in equipping them. Others move about with little control as they skirt back and forth in the current or even travel backwards! Most contestants finish the race, but a few founder on the shore. Win or lose, it is an exhilarating time for the rivaling racers and for the attentive audience.

DIRECTIONS Use the context of each sentence to write in the missing word. Then look back at the story to be sure your sentence gives the same meaning as the one in the story.

1. Every year in the month of May, a _____ is held in Wichita, Kansas, on the banks of the Arkansas River.

2. Thousands of people _____ to the river to see the art exhibits and hot-air balloons, and listen to concerts.

3. The highlight of the festival is a very _____ race.

4. Participants _____ down the river in bathtubs!

5. The _____ for the contestants are _____ .

6. The _____ must include an old-fashioned, cast-iron bathtub.

7. No _____ are allowed, although a sail is permitted.

8. No more than two people are allowed to row, pedal, paddle, or otherwise _____ the "boat" downstream.

9. Their entries may be _____ with decorations of wood, plastic, cloth, metal, etc.

DIRECTIONS Use context to circle *all* correct answers.

1. *Traverse* can mean:
   sail   travel
   stop   go

2. *Remarkable* can mean:
   odd   unusual
   common   uncommon

3. *Ingenuity* can mean:
   skill   creativity
   cleverness   rudeness

4. *Founder* can mean:
   win   fail
   succeed   collapse

5. *Rivaling* can mean:
   losing   dancing
   competing   walking

6. *Exhilarating* can mean:
   exciting   boring
   thrilling   breathtaking

7. *Flock* can mean:
   travel   come
   gather   leave

8. *Embellished* can mean:
   covered   decorated
   torn   destroyed

REMEMBER Use all the words to figure out an unknown word.

A Minor Misunderstanding

Would you be confused if you read this ad in your favorite magazine? In this lesson, you will learn about words with multiple meanings. You'll read about a multiple-meaning word that caused a misunderstanding.

> Watch for our discussion of the issue of curfews in our next issue which we will issue in two months!

1 KEYS to Multiple-Meaning Words

Some words can have several different meanings.

LEARN When a word has more than one meaning, we use words around it to tell which meaning was used. Look at the meanings of *issue*:

> **is·sue** (ish′o͞o) *n.* **1** a thing or group of things sent or given out [the July *issue* of a magazine]. **2** a problem to be talked over [The candidates will debate the *issues.*] *v.* **3** to give or deal out; distribute [The teacher *issued* new books.]

The words around *issue* tell you that the notice means there will be a discussion of the *topic* in the next *magazine* which will be *published* in two months.

DIRECTIONS Use the words around each underlined word to help you tell which meaning is meant. Circle the correct definition.

1. I was careful not to <u>gorge</u> myself at Thanksgiving dinner.
   narrow pass or valley   to overeat greedily

2. Mom went to the store to get some <u>staples</u> so we could bake cookies.
   a metal fastener   common items such as soap, milk, eggs

3. He was not very <u>patient</u> while waiting for the test results.
   able to wait without complaining   person under a doctor's care

4. Taking my little brother with me certainly <u>hampers</u> my social life.
   dirty clothes containers   makes it difficult

② Practice With Multiple Meanings

DIRECTIONS Use the words around each underlined word to help you decide which dictionary definition below best describes the word's meaning. Write the number on the line.

_____ **1.** Geoffrey has a <u>novel</u> idea we should definitely consider.

_____ **2.** Dad had to call the <u>service</u> department after all.

_____ **3.** My brother is no longer a <u>minor</u>.

_____ **4.** Here's a <u>passage</u> that tells about Jeb Stuart.

_____ **5.** The matter is of <u>prime</u> importance to my sister.

_____ **6.** The graduation <u>service</u> lasted nearly two hours.

_____ **7.** Look under the first letter of the next word if a book title begins with an <u>article</u>.

_____ **8.** My uncle is a <u>major</u> in the Air Force.

_____ **9.** My <u>passage</u> was due to start in eight hours and I didn't have my passport yet.

_____ **10.** There was a <u>slug</u> on the driveway after the rain.

_____ **11.** This <u>pitcher</u> has a chipped spout.

_____ **12.** The defendant maintained that someone wanted to <u>frame</u> him.

_____ **13.** He found that 1, 3, 5, 7, and 11 were <u>prime</u>.

_____ **14.** I was afraid they were going to <u>slug</u> it out.

_____ **15.** Have you read C. J. Lewis' last <u>novel</u>?

_____ **16.** Dad assisted, though the accident was a <u>minor</u> one.

_____ **17.** Have you carefully read this <u>article</u> about the Civil War?

_____ **18.** There are three <u>major</u> requirements to become a member.

_____ **19.** Bill will be the <u>pitcher</u> in the last game of the series.

_____ **20.** This <u>frame</u> is perfect for my ancestor's photograph.

ar·ti·cle **1.** a piece of writing on a single subject **2.** the words *a, an,* or *the*

nov·el **1.** unusual **2.** a long story, usually a book

slug **1.** to hit hard **2.** a small animal like a snail but with no shell

ser·vice **1.** work done for others **2.** a ceremony

pas·sage **1.** voyage **2.** part of a speech or a written work

frame **1.** border around a picture **2.** dishonest plan to make another appear guilty

pit·cher **1.** one who pitches the ball **2.** container to hold liquid

prime **1.** of great importance **2.** number divisible only by itself and one

mi·nor **1.** under the age of 18 or 21 **2.** of small importance

ma·jor **1.** outstanding or very important **2.** high military ranking

DIRECTIONS Read how one word with very different meanings almost caused a minor misunderstanding to become a major one.

Samantha was feeling so depressed. She'd been at Parnell for only two weeks and here she had caused herself to be more of an outsider than when she'd arrived on her first day. Many times her parents had cautioned her that a "chance remark" could be mistakenly interpreted by someone. Today it had happened, and Samantha felt sure that she was back on the fringes of the group. It looked as though her peers were avoiding her.

There was trouble and she was to blame. She knew she must right the wrong she had done so that she could go home with a clear conscience. The last thing she wanted to do was hurt Elizabeth. She glanced now to where Elizabeth sat with her broken leg propped on a chair.

"Why did I say that?" she thought. "I meant it to be a funny play on words. Maybe if they knew me better, they would have laughed." She knew, however, that her comment had been totally out of line.

It had happened before lunch when a group of the girls were talking about the class play and the tryouts later in the week. Sandy had said she'd been practicing for the part of the witch, and Elizabeth made the comment that she was going to try out for the part of Melody. Samantha, thinking more of the words than of the appropriateness of

her thoughts, chimed, "But, Elizabeth, you don't have to try out! You're already in the cast!" Elizabeth's face had gone from a radiant smile to a dark scowl, and the other girls had given Samantha harsh stares before abruptly moving away.

Now Samantha found herself again focusing on Elizabeth's cast. "What I have to do is wait for Elizabeth after school and apologize. Maybe I can make up for what I said by helping her carry her books." she thought. Then her gaze was met by Elizabeth's. Samantha smiled guiltily and was astonished when Elizabeth smiled back!

"Oh, maybe she understands!" thought Samantha. "I might not be in the doghouse, after all!" With that, Samantha dug out her spelling book. She silently promised herself to be much more careful with her words from now on.

DIRECTIONS Find and circle in the story each bold-faced word below. Use the words around it to help you decide its meaning. Circle the letter of the correct meaning. Then answer the questions below.

1. cast
    a. a group of actors and actresses
    b. a stiff plaster form

2. peers
    a. looks into
    b. friends or classmates

3. fringes
    a. outside edges of
    b. a decorative border of threads

4. depressed
    a. to press down
    b. sad or gloomy

5. might
    a. strength or power
    b. maybe

6. right
    a. correct
    b. the opposite of left

A. What did Samantha mean when she said, "I might not be in the doghouse, after all"? _____

_____

B. What does "to right a wrong" mean? _____

_____

REMEMBER Use context to get the meaning of a multiple-meaning word.

Words Working Overtime

Sometimes missing one of a word's meanings makes you miss all the fun! In this lesson, you'll have some fun as you learn to recognize words that put in more than their share of overtime.

1 KEYS to Multiple Meanings

One word can have many meanings.

 **LEARN** Jokes and riddles use words with double meanings.

DIRECTIONS Read the poem. Write the multiple-meaning word that makes each sentence a riddle.

Have you ever seen a sheet on a river bed?

1. _____

Or a single hair from a hammer's head?

2. _____

Has the foot of a mountain any toes?

3. _____

And is there a pair of garden hose?

4. _____

Does the needle ever wink its eye?

5. _____

Why doesn't the wing of a building fly?

6. _____

Can you tickle the ribs of a parasol?

7. _____

Or open the trunk of a tree at all?

8. _____

Are the teeth of a rake ever going to bite?

9. _____

Have the hands of a clock any left or right?

10. _____

Can the garden plot be deep and dark?

11. _____

And what is the sound of the birch's bark?

12. _____

2 Practice With Multiple Meanings

DIRECTIONS In each joke, circle the multiple-meaning word whose definitions are listed below. Which words in the joke make you think of each meaning? Write them on the line after the definition they suggest. The first one is done for you.

1. Doctors must have a sense of humor because they leave their patients in (stitches.)

   laughing _humor_

   sewn
   wounds _doctors/patients_

2. Pitching is like war. The winning team usually has the best arms.

   weapons _____

   parts of the
   body _____

3. I caught a really big catfish yesterday but couldn't weigh it because it had no scales.

   devices for
   weighing _____

   outer cover-
   ing of fish _____

4. Trees are usually quiet, but I've heard that the dogwood's bark is worse than its bite.

   outer cover-
   ing of trees _____

   sound a dog
   makes _____

5. Once there was a man who thought he would like having a farm in Kansas but found out it was just plain work.

   ordinary _____

   large stretch
   of flat land _____

6. Maybe they call it cast iron because if it falls on you, it will break your bones.

   molded or
   shaped _____

   stiff plaster
   form _____

7. We know a golfer who got a hunting license because he excelled at shooting birdies.

   score in golf _____

   small child's
   word for
   flying fowl _____

DIRECTIONS Read about Jerry's act for the class talent show. Circle any word whose double meaning is part of a joke.

With the class talent show only two days off, Jerry was starting to worry. He had no act. His singing was poor, he couldn't play a musical instrument, and he had never learned to dance. What could he possibly do that would entertain a room full of fifth graders?

Suddenly he had an idea. He would tell jokes. He had never cared for long, story-like jokes. He preferred puns, short jokes that used the same word in two ways. Jerry knew there were several books of puns in his school library. He copied the ones he liked best and then began to learn them for the show.

Jerry's puns made him the star of the show! He shared the spotlight with the others, however, and made no attempt to hog the stage. After all, he was no ham.

---

1. Why did the nervous carpenter have to visit a dentist? (He bit his nails too much.)

2. When the frog joined the baseball team, why did he play in the outfield? (Because he was good at catching flies.)

3. Why are boll weevils so tired at night? (Because they spend all day at the plant.)

4. What job did Dracula's son have with the baseball team? (Bat boy.)

5. Some say it's so cold at hockey games that there's really no need for fans.

6. Why was the strawberry so worried? (Because it was in quite a jam.)

7. Why did the soldier refuse to go skin diving? (He didn't think he could carry a tank on his back.)

Look for words with double meanings as you read this American Folk Rhyme. On the lines below, write the two meanings that you need to think about for each word in order to see the poem's humor.

Foolish Questions

Where can a man buy a cap for his knee?
Or a key for the lock of his hair?
And can his eyes be called a school?
I would think—there are pupils there!
What jewels are found in the crown of his head,
And who walks on the bridge of his nose?
Can he use, in building the roof of his mouth,
The nails on the ends of his toes?
Can the crook of his elbow be sent to jail—
If it can, well, then, what did it do?
And how does he sharpen his shoulder blades?
I'll be hanged if I know—do you?
Can he sit in the shade of the palm of his hand,
And beat time with the drum in his ear?
Can the calf of his leg eat the corn on his toe?—
There's somethin' pretty strange around here!

—adapted by William Cole

1. cap _____

    cap _____

2. palm _____

    palm _____

3. crown _____

    crown _____

4. lock _____

    lock _____

5. roof _____

    roof _____

6. crook _____

    crook _____

7. calf _____

    calf _____

8. drum _____

    drum _____

9. pupils _____

    pupils _____

10. bridge _____

    bridge _____

REMEMBER Watch out for words with double meanings!

Thanks To A Fly

Some words are like chameleons, those tropical lizards that change color to match their surroundings. In this lesson, you'll learn about words whose meanings depend on how they're used in a sentence. You'll also learn about the invention of graph paper.

KEYS to Multiple Meanings

Some words can be used to mean several different things.

EXAMPLE Words like *run* and *present* have more than one meaning and can be used as more than one part of speech.

He scored the team's first *run* because he could *run* so fast.

In this sentence, *run* is first a noun and then a verb.

Mayor Thorp will *present* the *present*.

Present is first a verb, meaning *to give,* and then, pronounced differently, as a noun meaning *a gift*.

DIRECTIONS Read each sentence. Write *noun* or *verb* on the line to show how the underlined word is used.

1. The <u>store</u> received my check. _____

2. You must <u>number</u> the boxes to get them in order. _____

3. We will <u>store</u> our furniture for two months. _____

4. Mom is going to <u>wallpaper</u> my room. _____

5. I'm too old now for juvenile <u>wallpaper</u>. _____

6. There's no <u>number</u> on this envelope. _____

2 Practice With Multiple Meanings

DIRECTIONS Read each sentence. Mark an X in the correct column to show if the underlined word is used as a noun or as a verb.

Noun	Verb	
1. _____	_____	It was a rather long <u>climb</u> up the mountain.
2. _____	_____	We had to <u>walk</u> to the auditorium in the rain.
3. _____	_____	The flood water <u>rose</u> five feet in one hour!
4. _____	_____	The store will <u>bill</u> me for my purchases.
5. _____	_____	The canoes were usually made of <u>bark</u>.
6. _____	_____	He asked me to <u>state</u> my surname.
7. _____	_____	She tried to clean and <u>fix</u> her rusty bike.
8. _____	_____	The rope was <u>strong</u> and secure.
9. _____	_____	We sent the boxes by express <u>truck</u>.
10. _____	_____	Just <u>watch</u> how easily this is assembled!

Noun	Verb	
11. _____	_____	First you have to <u>climb</u> up the rope ladder.
12. _____	_____	A long <u>walk</u> will be good exercise for Grandpa.
13. _____	_____	A <u>rose</u> might be any of several colors.
14. _____	_____	The senate vetoed the controversial <u>bill</u>.
15. _____	_____	The dog will surely <u>bark</u> if a prowler is out there.
16. _____	_____	We moved here from a neighboring <u>state</u>.
17. _____	_____	We'll be in a horrible <u>fix</u> if the electricity fails.
18. _____	_____	Bill can single-handedly <u>rope</u> a steer.
19. _____	_____	We'll have to <u>truck</u> this load up the incline.
20. _____	_____	My <u>watch</u> probably needs a new battery.

Read and Apply

DIRECTIONS Read about the contribution of a common housefly.

Have you ever graphed a point onto a piece of graph paper? To do so, you must use two numbers known as the point's coordinates. The first of the two numbers tells how far to the left or right the point is located. The second tells how far up or down. To find the point with coordinates (4,7), for instance, you would move to the right four units and then move up seven more units. The point is shown in this graph:

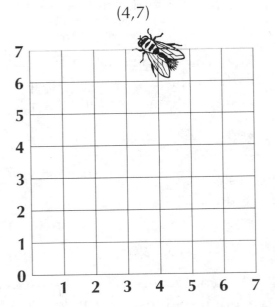

(4,7)

Graphing points in this way is common now, but no one had heard of it three centuries ago. It was then that a young boy in France discovered how to graph points while lying in bed one day. The boy was very rich and most people thought that he was quite lazy, since he liked to recline in bed until late hours. What people did not know was that while he appeared to be loafing, the boy was thinking!

One morning he spent many minutes watching a fly as it walked about on the ceiling over his head. Suddenly an idea hit him.

"Why, I could tell the position of that fly anywhere on the ceiling with only two numbers!" he said aloud. He then imagined that his ceiling was a piece of paper numbered on each side. The two numbers he mentioned were the coordinates of the point where the fly was located. The boy's discovery led to the idea of graphing points—all thanks to an ordinary housefly!

DIRECTIONS Read each sentence. Then complete the statements about the sentence by circling the best word in each set of parentheses.

1. Suddenly an idea hit him.

   a. The word *hit* is used as a (*noun/ verb*).

   b. *Hit* means (*score/to strike*).

2. The point is shown in this graph.

   a. The word *graph* is used as a (*noun/verb*).

   b. *Graph* means (*to chart/a chart*).

3. He thought of the ceiling as having numbers on each side.

   a. The word *side* is used as a (*noun/verb*).

   b. *Side* means (*edge or border/to favor*).

4. They were the coordinates of the point where the fly was located.

   a. The word *point* is used as a (*noun/verb*).

   b. *Point* means (*a specific spot/to direct attention to*).

DIRECTIONS Read about the uses of each underlined word. Then write a sentence to show each use.

1. The word <u>advocate</u> can be used as a verb to mean *strongly suggest* or as a noun to mean *one who strongly supports.*

   noun: _____

   _____

   verb: _____

   _____

2. The word <u>book</u> can be used as a verb to mean *to schedule* or as a noun to mean *something to read.*

   verb: _____

   _____

   noun: _____

   _____

3. The word <u>staple</u> can be used as a noun to mean *a metal fastener* or as a verb to mean *fasten together with a metal piece.*

   verb: _____

   _____

   noun: _____

   _____

4. The word <u>maneuver</u> can be used as a noun to mean *a carefully-made plan* or as a verb to mean *to plan for a purpose.*

   noun: _____

   _____

   verb: _____

   _____

REMEMBER A word's meaning may depend on how it's used.

Home Run Helen

Sometimes it helps to try fresh ideas. In this lesson, you will read about a girl whose new ideas helped her softball team go to the top of the league. You will also learn about words with more than one meaning.

KEYS to Multiple Meanings

Which meaning makes sense in the sentence?

LEARN   Many words have more than one meaning. To know which meaning is being used, read the sentence to see which meaning makes sense.

EXAMPLE   If you read *I feel blue today,* you can tell from reading the whole sentence that the word *blue* does not mean a color. It means *sad* or *depressed.*

DIRECTIONS The word *down* can have any of these meanings:

1. in cash

2. get serious

3. toward the bottom

4. soft fluffy feathers

5. a football play

Read each sentence below and decide which meaning of *down* is being used. Write its number on the line. Use each meaning once.

_____ **A.** My pillow is stuffed with goose down.

_____ **B.** The team's completed pass gave it a first down.

_____ **C.** My parents made a $500 down payment on a new car.

_____ **D.** The teacher told the class to settle down to work.

_____ **E.** The plane has just touched down.

② Practice With Multiple Meanings

DIRECTIONS Read the multiple meanings of the word *set:*

1. to lay in a certain position.
2. to put in order or arrange
3. to assign to certain positions
4. to arrange type for printing
5. to decide in advance
6. to write words that fit music or music to fit words
7. things that belong together
8. to wave or curl the hair
9. a formation in some dances
10. to harden or become solid
11. ready to begin
12. to assign the action of a play to a certain place

DIRECTIONS Decide which of the above meanings of *set* is meant in each of the sentences below. Write its number on the line before the sentence. Then rewrite the sentence so that it makes sense without using the word *set*. The first one is done for you.

__5__ 1. The time for recess was set by the principal.
The time for recess was decided by the principal.

_____ 2. Dave set the book on the shelf.

_____ 3. On your mark, get set, go!

_____ 4. Guards were set all along the border.

_____ 5. The letters were set in very small print.

_____ 6. I need a shampoo and set before I go to the party.

_____ 7. Mom bought a new set of dishes.

_____ 8. The doctor set the broken bone.

3 Read and Apply

DIRECTIONS Think about the different meanings of the word *run* as you read this story about how Helen helped her team win.

"We looked like a circus act out there today!" exclaimed Tracy. "Sometimes I feel like quitting. It's so depressing to lose every softball game!"

"I know, Tracy," Helen agreed. "I feel the same way, but it's not like either of us to *run* (1) from a problem. Maybe we need to make some changes. Why don't we meet with the team to talk it over."

The girls called a meeting at Helen's house that afternoon. A decision was made to choose a team captain. When Tracy nominated Helen to *run* (2) for the position, she was unanimously elected.

Helen suggested two ways to tackle their *run* (3) of losses. All the girls agreed they could use a good coach and more practice time. Unfortunately, no one knew any qualified person to coach them.

The team decided to *run* (4) this ad in the local paper:

Wanted. Coach to *run* (5) girls' softball team. Experience required. Call Helen, 555-1736.

The very first night the ad appeared, Helen got a call from a Ms. Leeman who explained that she had recently moved here but had coached a girls' team the past several years in her previous town. Helen asked Ms. Leeman to come to her home to meet with her to discuss the team's needs. It turned out the team had found its coach!

Ms. Leeman watched the team play the next evening and then began to make some position and batting order changes. At the next scheduled game, the girls played like a well-*run* (6) machine. The new techniques seemed to have added to everyone's confidence.

Soon the team was in second place in their league, but Helen was not content to *run* (7) second and Ms. Leeman agreed. She and Helen urged the team to go for the championship, and by the last game, they were tied for first place.

The final game was tough because the two teams were so evenly matched. When Helen's team came to bat in the second half of the last inning, the score was tied, 1–1.

"One *run* (8) will do it!" yelled Helen to her teammates. "Come on, girls, just one run!"

Tracy was first at bat. She struck out. Then Harriet hit a long fly to center field. It was caught. Two outs, and Helen was up next. She walked to the plate, determined to get a hit. It was so hot that sweat had begun to *run* (9) down her cheeks, but she forced herself to concentrate. When the first pitch came, she knew it was the one she wanted. She swung with all her strength. She felt the glorious sting of the bat striking the ball. She began to *run* (10) as fast as she could. As she was rounding second base, she heard her teammates screaming, "Home run, Helen! Home run, Helen!"

Helen glanced over her shoulder. She had slammed that ball clear over the fence. She had hit a home run and her team had won the title!

DIRECTIONS Choose the correct meaning from the list below for each use of the word *run* in the story. Write the letter of the meaning next to that number below.

A. move the legs rapidly to go

B. to operate or work (as a machine)

C. to flee

D. to be a candidate for a position

E. a point scored in baseball or softball

F. to flow from melting

G. to publish as in a newspaper

H. to manage or supervise

I. to finish a contest in a certain place (to run last)

J. a series (a run of luck)

1. _____   2. _____   3. _____   4. _____   5. _____

6. _____   7. _____   8. _____   9. _____   10. _____

REMEMBER A word's meaning may depend on the words around it.

Coining Words

Many words in the English language come from people of different nationalities, but some were made up or "coined." In this lesson, you will learn how words can be combined to create new words.

 ## KEYS to Compound and Blended Words

New words can be made from two common words.

LEARN   A compound word is made when two whole words are combined. A blended word is made by combining parts of two other words.

EXAMPLE   The word *daylight* is a compound word made from the words *day* and *light.* The word *smog* is a blended word made from part of the word *smoke* and part of the word *fog.*

DIRECTIONS   Use the list of words at the right to form some compound words. Write the new words on the lines.

1. _____ , watch   night

2. _____   rise   dog

3. _____   sun   over

DIRECTIONS   Combine the words on the left to form blended words. Write the new words on the lines.

1. television + marathon =   _____

2. breakfast + lunch =   _____

3. motor + hotel =   _____

2 Practice With Compound and Blended Words

DIRECTIONS Each of the words below is a compound or blended word. Write the two words used to make the new word. These words may help you: automatic, laundry, marathon, squirm, wiggle.

1. swimathon   _____   _____

2. wheelchair   _____   _____

3. squiggle   _____   _____

4. laundromat   _____   _____

5. skyscraper   _____   _____

6. chalkboard   _____   _____

7. gasohol   _____   _____

8. grandparent   _____   _____

DIRECTIONS Write *compound* or *blend* on the line to tell if each numbered word above is a compound or a blended word.

1. _____   5. _____

2. _____   6. _____

3. _____   7. _____

4. _____   8. _____

DIRECTIONS Make up your own blended words.

1. What would you call it?

    a. a cross between a tiger and a lion   _____

    b. a cross between a horse and a zebra   _____

    c. a cross between a laugh and a giggle   _____

    d. a restaurant serving only sandwiches   _____

2. What monster's name could be used for a place that sells frankfurters and serves

    pop in German glasses called steins? _____

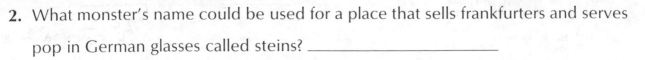

Read and Apply

Read about how some interesting words have come to be.

When a scientist makes a discovery or a company introduces a brand new product, the need for a new word arises. While the English language already contains hundreds of thousands of words, these are not enough to be useful in totally new situations. For example, when computers were first developed, their inventors needed a term to describe the smallest amount of information these machines could handle. This amount, called a binary unit, was shortened by combining the first part of the word *binary* with the last part of the word *unit* to produce the word *bit*.

When cattle researchers created a new type of meat by breeding ordinary beef cattle with buffalos, they called the result beefalo. When biologists studied a new variety of cat whose parents were a lion and a tiger, they called the cub a liger. Other mixed forms of plants and animals include a dog called a cockapoo, which is part cocker spaniel and part poodle, and a fruit known as a tangelo which is part tangerine and part grapefruit (which is also known as a pomelo).

These blended words account for three of every hundred new words introduced into English each year. We like these words because they're clever and call our attention to the words used to create them. It is for just this reason that many blends are coined—to grab people's attention.

A popular writer once created a fantasy animal known as a snark. It was supposed to be half snake and half shark. Another strange animal was the hippogator which was part hippopotamus and part alligator.

Study each pair of words. Find the blended word from the story. Write it on the line.

1. beef + buffalo

_____

2. lion + tiger

_____

3. cocker + poodle

_____

4. binary + unit

_____

5. tangerine + pomelo

_____

6. hippopotamus + alligator

_____

7. snake + shark

_____

DIRECTIONS Complete an interplanetary traveler's diary entry. Write a compound word on each line.

I, being a very intelligent and word-wise traveler, visited the planet Earth. I find I must report a peculiar characteristic of some of the inhabitants. They have an odd habit of joining small words to make larger words. They call it making compound words, but, to tell you the truth, I think it's truly bizarre! I mean, it seems so elementary to just combine two words!

Take the special home where their dog sleeps, for example. Apparently they have no unique word for it, so they simply call it a _____. Then you go into those earthling's houses and you notice, if you listen carefully (as I always do), that they refer to brushes they use on their hair and teeth as _____ and

_____. One would surely think there'd be fancier names for such weird contraptions! Oh, and then I couldn't help but overhear (Whoops, this compound word stuff is surely contagious!) one of the miniature earthlings complaining about having to wash his face with a _____ and clean his teeth with some stuff in a tube that he called _____.

In summary, I am simply astounded at the number of extra words they have made from simply combining two smaller words. I'd really like to sneak a look at the wordbook (There I go again!) they call a dictionary and count all the compound words they use. Maybe next trip!

REMEMBER A word may be made from two other words.

Rooftops of the World

Knowing the meanings of common prefixes helps you decode unfamiliar words. In this lesson, you will learn to decode new words by looking for specific groups of letters attached before words. You'll read about some rooftops quite unlike the one over your house.

1 KEYS to Prefixes

A prefix changes a root word's meaning.

LEARN A prefix, like a word, has its own meaning. Unlike a word, however, a prefix never stands alone. A prefix always comes at the beginning of a word. Here are some common prefixes and their meanings:

pre	=	before		sub	=	under
un	=	not		inter	=	between
re	=	again		mis	=	wrong
over	=	above		dis	=	do the opposite of
in	=	not		geo	=	earth

EXAMPLE Adding a prefix to a common root word changes the root word's meaning. To *interpret* something is *to understand* it. Adding the prefix *mis* to the word, however, creates a new word that means *to get the wrong understanding*.

DIRECTIONS Use the above prefixes and their meanings to match the words below with their definitions. Write the letter on the line.

_____ 1. interstellar   **A.** not enough

_____ 2. submarine   **B.** between stars

_____ 3. misconduct   **C.** under the water

_____ 4. insufficient   **D.** wrong behavior

_____ 5. overestimate   **E.** to guess too high

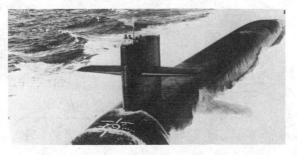

2 Practice With Prefixes

DIRECTIONS One of the words in each sentence below is not complete. Circle the missing prefix to complete the word. Then write the prefix on the line so the sentence makes sense.

1. Marty was sure that she had been

   given some _____
   information when she found
   herself hopelessly lost.

      re   un   mis

2. What _____ graphical area
   are you studying now?

      pre   geo   mis

3. The customers became _____
   ruly and grabbed at the bargain
   merchandise.

      sub   in   un

4. I could tell she was _____
   interested in the details of my trip
   when she turned and walked
   away.

      pre   mis   dis

5. He appears to be _____
   sensitive to the feelings of others.

      dis   pre   in

6. The new student is _____
   acting with the others quite well.

      inter   dis   geo

7. The weather must be pretty

   humid in _____ tropical
   regions.

      sub   mis   pre

8. They are not communicating right

   now due to some _____
   resolved differences.

      re   over   un

9. Do not _____ judge the
   movie until you've at least heard
   what it's about.

      un   pre   re

10. He definitely _____ stated
    his argument.

       in   over   un

Read and Apply

DIRECTIONS Look for words with prefixes as you read this article about rooftops of the world.

Rising higher than cities, higher than trees can grow and higher than most living things, are the "rooftops of the world." These barren, inhospitable places are the highest points of the earth.

Few geologists disagree when it is said that mountains were formed in prehistoric times. Subterranean forces within the earth pressed the land in two different directions at once. These slow but unstoppable forces caused the ground to rise to great heights. Some mountains have even risen since man has been on the earth. Such are the Andes Mountains of South America where vineyards have been discovered at elevations where grapes cannot grow today.

The world's highest mountains are the Himalayas of Central Asia. Mount Everest, long believed to be the tallest mountain on earth, is there. Many mountain climbers attempted to conquer Everest before its peak was finally reached in 1953 by Edmund Hillary. His expedition measured the height of Mount Everest at 29,028 feet above sea level. According to one story, Hillary's first measurement was exactly 29,000 feet. He recalculated the height, however, since he feared that some would not believe he had truly reached the top if he reported such an even figure.

Mountains, regardless of their heights, may be very difficult to climb because of unusual shapes. The Matterhorn, in Switzerland, is only 14,690 feet but it poses real problems for climbers because of its straight cliffs that rise directly overhead and forbid even the slightest miscalculation.

Some mountains are not easily climbed because they are inaccessible. The highest peak in Antarctica, Mount Vison Massif, for example, is a mere 16,864 feet high. Yet climbers do not readily attempt to scale it. Why? Because a climber must first travel across a thousand miles of polar ice just to reach its base!

Perhaps the most remote mountain peak of all will challenge members of some future generation of interplanetary mountain climbers. This peak is a volcano discovered on the planet Mars. It rises to a height of over 80,000 feet, nearly three times the elevation of Everest! Mountains, then, it would seem, are rooftops not only of our world, but of other worlds as well.

DIRECTIONS Look in the story you just read for a word with a prefix to match each meaning below. Write the word on the line.

1. _____ means below the ground.

2. _____ means scientists who study the earth.

3. _____ means before recorded history.

4. _____ means not able to be halted.

5. _____ means not friendly.

6. _____ means between the planets.

7. _____ means above eye level.

8. _____ means a wrong computation.

9. _____ means the opposite of agree.

DIRECTIONS Now use your understanding of prefixes to write a definition of the following words:

1. unusual _____

2. inconvenient _____

3. recalculate _____

4. discover _____

5. overprice _____

REMEMBER Prefixes begin many words.

Protecting A New Idea

Suppose you created something no one else had ever thought of. Can it be protected from those who might copy it? In this lesson, you will read about how people protect new products and ideas with patents and trademarks. You'll also learn about the use of suffixes.

1 KEYS to Suffixes

A suffix is an addition to the end of a root word.

LEARN The addition of a suffix to the end of a root word changes the meaning of the word and may also change the root word's spelling. A word may have more than one suffix.

EXAMPLE The lawn was *beautifully landscaped.*

The *y* in the root word *beauty* was changed to *i* before the suffixes *ful* and *ly* were added. The final *e* was dropped in the root word *landscape* before the suffix *ed* was added.

DIRECTIONS Read each root word and the word formed by adding a suffix. Circle the suffix. Write *changed* or *unchanged* on the line to tell if the root word's spelling was changed when a suffix was added.

1. motion / motioning _____

2. use / usable _____

3. calculate / calculator _____

4. invent / invention _____

5. populate / population _____

6. price / pricelessness _____

7. suffix / suffixes _____

8. convince / convincing _____

DIRECTIONS Read each sentence. Think about the spelling of the underlined word and write *changed* or *unchanged* to complete part *a*. Complete part *b* to tell how the word's meaning was changed.

1. A patent protects an *invention* for a certain number of years.
   a. When the suffix *tion* was added, the root word's spelling was

   _____.

   b. The suffix changed the root word from a verb, meaning *to create something new,* to a noun meaning

   _____.

2. For an invention to be *patentable,* it must be an original idea that would not be obvious to just anyone.
   a. The root word's spelling was

   _____

   when the suffix *able* was added.
   b. The suffix changed the root

   word, _____,

   from a noun or verb to an adjective, meaning *able to be protected.*

3. The *substitution* of nylon cloth for canvas cloth in tent making would not be a patentable idea.
   a. The spelling of *substitute* was

   _____

   when the suffix *tion* was added.
   b. The root word was changed from a verb, meaning *to put in place of* to a noun, meaning

   _____

4. *Companies* or individuals use trademarks to protect the name or logo of their product or service.
   a. The addition of *es*

   _____

   the spelling.
   b. The root word was changed from a singular noun to a

   _____ noun.

5. An inventor must apply to the federal *government* to gain a trademark or patent.
   a. The root word's spelling was

   _____.

   b. The root word was changed

   from a _____,

   meaning *to rule* to a

   _____,

   meaning *a ruling group.*

6. An inventor's *creation* can be protected in many countries if an application for a patent or trademark is filed in each country.
   a. The root word's spelling was

   _____.

   b. The root word meaning *to make something* was a

   _____,

   but *creation* is a noun.

Read and Apply

DIRECTIONS Read about protecting a new idea.

Roxanne's mom was an inventor of sorts. She was always puttering with something in her "creative den," as she called it. One day she emerged with a look on her face that resembled the expression she'd worn for weeks after she'd revealed her first "Nothing Box," a clever contraption for entertaining oneself when having nothing to do. This time, however, Roxanne's mom held up a large stuffed doll that looked like a loveable old grandfather.

"What'd you create this time, Mom?"

"This, my dear, is a Popol! Does it look like anything you've ever seen before?" said her mother, excitedly.

"It looks like a grandpa, Mom! He's adorable! Will you get a patent on him like you did on the 'Nothing Box'? Will they be sold in all the stores?"

"The answer to your first question is yes. I'll start the application process to gain a patent tomorrow. I'll also have to apply for a trademark on this one, though, because I want to protect this fellow's name as well as the way he looks, and yes, I certainly hope the Popols will be in all the stores!"

"What's a trademark?" asked Roxanne.

"A trademark distinguishes the name, Popol, as my own idea and one that no one else can use. People will see the way it's written here on this fellow and soon be recognizing it, or so I hope. No one else is entitled to use those words or symbols appearing that way once they're protected by trademarks."

"How is that different from the patents you've gotten for your other things, Mom?"

"Well, a trademark protects the special name, Roxanne, while a patent gives the inventor control over the actual invention for a certain number of years, during which time no one else in the country can make or sell that specific thing."

"You remember meeting Miss Turner, the patent attorney, don't you?" her mom went on. "She specializes in assisting inventors and companies to be sure that new ideas are properly protected. She'll do an exhaustive search to make sure no one else in this country has already patented such a creature as Popol here and that no one has previously used his name. All this searching takes time. I know you've seen things that have 'Patent Pending' or 'Patent Applied For' on them. That's what I'll be putting on my Popols from the time I apply for the patent until it is, hopefully, granted. Then I'll put a small 'TM' to the right of the word, Popol, to show that I have applied for a trademark."

"Wow, Mom? Popol's awesome! All my friends will want one!"

"Great! The only thing an inventor loves more than an invention, is lots of 'ready consumers'!"

DIRECTIONS Find each numbered word in the story and circle it. Then write the root word and its suffix or suffixes on the lines. The first one is done for you.

	Root Word	Suffix
1. specializes	special	ize / s
2. hopefully		
3. gotten		
4. exhaustive		
5. adorable		
6. resembled		
7. puttering		
8. distinguishes		
9. emerged		
10. written		
11. creative		
12. excitedly		
13. entitled		
14. companies		

REMEMBER Suffixes change a word's meaning, and sometimes its spelling.

Deadly Disguise

Disguises sometimes require real detective work. In this lesson, you'll learn to detect well-disguised root words as you read about a deadly insect.

△1 KEYS to Prefixes and Suffixes

Some words are root words plus a prefix and suffix.

LEARN A common root word may be well disguised when a prefix and a suffix are added. The prefix and suffix change the root word's meaning.

EXAMPLE

prefix	+	root	+	suffix
immovable =	im	+	mov(e)	+	able

The word *move* means *to put in a different place*. The prefix *im* means *not* and the suffix *able* means *can be done*. The word *immovable* means *not able to be put in a different place*.

Notice that the spelling of the root word may be changed when a suffix is added.

DIRECTIONS Each of the words in the box has a disguised root word. Write the word beside its root word below.

disfigured	repositioned	misguided	undeniable

deny _____   position _____

figure _____   guide _____

2 Practice With Prefixes and Suffixes

DIRECTIONS Find the root word in each longer word below. Consider its meaning and the meanings of its prefix and suffix. Find the correct description of the word in the column at the right. Write the letter in the blank before the word. If you are correct, your answers will spell the topic of the story on the next page.

_____ 1. uneventful

_____ 2. superconductor

_____ 3. reinfection

_____ 4. encampment

_____ 5. unfairness

_____ 6. predarkness

_____ 7. unhappiness

_____ 8. declawed

_____ 9. semiworthless

_____ 10. unevenness

_____ 11. exchangeable

W. dusk

o. not very valuable

c. place to pitch a tent

w. not smoothness

B. boring

i. sadness

k. not playing by the rules

d. can't scratch anymore

l. electricity flows smoothly

a. getting sick again

s. can be returned

What deadly insect's name did you spell? _____

Read and Apply

DIRECTIONS Look for root words disguised by prefixes and suffixes as you read about the deadliest spider of them all.

The supervenomous spiders in stories simply don't exist, but some real eight-legged creatures are to be avoided at all costs! Experts believe that the black widow, found in the Americas, Hawaii, and the Carribbean, is the deadliest.

Although the male black widow is nonthreatening, the female's bite is extremely deadly. A human who is bitten can suffer some very uncomfortable symptoms such as sweating, nervousness, and unbearable pain.

The actual number of black widow spider-bite victims is unknown, since many bites go unreported. Of those reported, about six victims in a hundred die. Generally, this percentage represents people who were already unusually ill or were very old. It's no wonder the poison has such ill effects, since it has been shown to be fifteen times as deadly as rattlesnake venom!

Scientists studying the black widow have uncovered some strange facts. For example, this spider seems to be much deadlier in the fall than in the spring. The female's bite in the fall, then, would be the worst of all possible situations. The female presents another hazard in that her eggs are also highly poisonous.

Though black widows are shy and do not attack unless frightened, they are undoubtedly dangerous and truly do deserve their title of "world's deadliest spider."

DIRECTIONS Look for words in the article you just read that follow this pattern:

PREFIX + ROOT + SUFFIX

Underline the root word in each word you find. Now think about its meaning and look to see if that meaning is listed below. If so, write the root word on the line and then write the word you read that was made by adding a prefix and suffix to the root. The first one is done for you.

Meaning of Root	Root	Word from Article
1. poison	venom	supervenomous
2. common		
3. tell		
4. warn		
5. lack of pain		
6. put up with		
7. one-hundredth		
8. hide		
9. question		

DIRECTIONS Write one of the above words with its prefix and suffix to complete each sentence below.

1. Strangely enough, some spider bites go _____ .

2. The male black widow's bite is _____ .

3. The black widow is _____ the deadliest spider.

4. A spider-bite victim experiences _____ pain.

5. A truly _____ _____ spider is the black widow.

6. A large _____ of spider-bite victims do not die

7. Research has _____ some facts about black widows.

8. The symptoms of spider bite victims are extremely _____ .

REMEMBER Finding a root word can help to recognize a bigger word.

Comparing Things

How do you feel when you get an excellent grade on a test? Is it the way you feel when you score a goal or a basket in soccer or basketball? In this lesson, you'll learn about analogies, which are special comparisons where the relationships are similar.

 KEYS to Analogies

An analogy shows two similar relationships.

LEARN Excellent is to test as goal is to soccer.

In this analogy, the first two underlined words have the same relationship as the last two. You feel super when you earn an excellent grade just like you feel super when you score for your team. An analogy can also be written using colons instead of the words *is to*. A double colon is used in place of the word *as*.

Excellent : test :: goal : soccer

DIRECTIONS Use a word from the word box to complete each analogy. Then fill in the blanks to write each analogy another way.

1. Doctor is to patient as teacher is to _____ .

   Doctor : _____ : : teacher : _____

2. _____ are to circus as musicians are to concert.

   _____ : circus :: _____ : concert

3. General is to specific as soup is to _____ .

   _____ : _____ :: soup : _____

> performers
> vegetable
> pupil

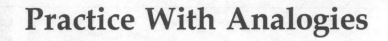

2 Practice With Analogies

DIRECTIONS Read the words in the box above each group of sentences. Write one of the words to complete each analogy.

| dribble | paragraph | masculine | secretary | Illinois |

1. Word : sentence :: sentence : _____ .

2. Chicago : _____ :: St. Louis : Missouri.

3. Screwdriver : carpenter :: typewriter : _____ .

4. _____ : basketball :: kick : football.

5. Female : feminine :: male : _____ .

| identical | drink | father | computer | novelist |

1. Mother : maternal :: _____ : paternal.

2. Starvation : eat :: dehydration : _____ .

3. Input : _____ :: picture : frame.

4. Poem : poet :: novel : _____ .

5. _____ : same :: fraternal : different.

| South America | enormous | future | triplets | definition |

1. Beautiful : pretty :: _____ : big.

2. Dictionary : _____ :: thesaurus : synonym.

3. Canada : North America :: Brazil : _____ .

4. Double : twins :: triple : _____ .

5. Today : present :: tomorrow : _____ .

Read and Apply

DIRECTIONS Read how Rich solved his own problem.

As Stephen approached the table in the corner of the library, he heard Rich sigh heavily.

"What's up, Rich? Ready to go pop some flies?"

"Uh, you'd better go on without me. The guys will be waiting and I might never get out to play," Rich responded gloomily. "This reading homework is really bad news! These analogies, or whatever they're called, are so hard! They're as bad as doing fractions in math. I just can't do them!"

"Analogies? What do you mean you can't do them? You just did!"

"Oh, no, I didn't! Look, I have a whole page of them and not one is done. I'll *never* understand how to do them!"

"But you just used an analogy, Rich. You said that doing analogies in reading is like doing fractions in math."

"So? That's what I said, all right!" snapped Rich.

"So, you can do analogies. Listen to yourself! An analogy is just comparing things like you just compared a part of reading to a part of math. They have the same relationship."

"Hmmm, I did say that, didn't I!" admitted Rich. "Let's see then, if analogies are to reading as fractions are to math, then exercise is to healthy as oxygen is to, uh . . . ?"

"Think about it, Rich. What's the relationship of exercise to being healthy?"

"You have to have exercise to be healthy, and you have to have oxygen to *live!* Hey, I got it, didn't I?" asked Rich hopefully.

"You sure did! What's the next one?" coached his friend.

"Aluminum is to metal as corduroy is to . . . fabric?" asked Rich.

"You got it! Keep going, Rich! The guys are waiting!"

Circle the word that completes the analogy. Write it on the line.

1. 'Goodbye' is to depart as 'hello' is

   to _____ .

   greeting   leave
   arrive   hug

2. Screws are to

   _____

   as nails are to hammers.

   wood   screwdrivers
   bolts   carpenters

3. Saxophone is to woodwind as

   _____

   is to brass.

   trumpet   reed
   music   song

4. Yawn is to sleepy as perspire is to

   _____ .

   sweat   tired
   muscle   hot

5. Rectangles are to triangles as

   _____ are to
   triplets.

   twins   quintuplets
   squares   quadruplets

6. _____ : holes
   :: bandages : wounds.

   people   fractures
   patches   casts

7. Kangaroo : rabbit ::

   perch : _____ .

   goldfish   elephant
   eagle   chimpanzee

8. Rabies : veterinarian ::

   influenza : _____ .

   dentist   physician
   accountant   stockbroker

9. Spaghetti : pasta ::

   _____ : mineral.

   lasagna   macaroni
   petunia   calcium

10. Input : output ::

    _____ : withdraw.

    deposit   money
    computer   account

11. Northernmost is to Arctic as

    _____

    is to Antarctic.

    western   outermost
    southernmost uppermost

12. _____
    : temperature :: speedometer :
    speed.

    mathematics   geometry
    thermometer   distance

What Do I Do Next?

Your macaroni and cheese is more like macaroni soup! What happened? In this lesson you'll learn about following directions to prevent such disappointing results.

1 KEYS to Following Directions

Take it one step at a time!

LEARN   Remember these tips when following directions.

- Read or listen carefully to get every part of the directions.
- Follow the directions in order, one step at a time.
- Check progress as you go along.

EXAMPLE   Compare the directions for making macaroni and cheese with what you did. Circle the number of the step that was left out.

Directions

1. Cook macaroni in boiling water until tender.
2. Drain macaroni.
3. Add milk, butter and cheese.
4. Stir together and serve.

What I did

1. Cooked macaroni in boiling water until tender.
2. Added milk, butter and cheese.
3. Stirred together.

DIRECTIONS Circle the numbers of any steps in the directions that explain why Alan got lost.

Directions

1. Go two blocks past the park.
2. Turn right.
3. Go the the first stop sign.
4. Go left to the gas station.

What Alan did

1. Went two blocks past the park.
2. Went to the second stop sign.
3. Turned left.

DIRECTIONS It is helpful to list directions in order step-by-step so you can easily see which step is to be done next. This helps you check your progress as you go along.

Use the tips you've learned about following directions to help Bettye write out her teacher's directions for the class's outing on Sunday, in step-by-step form.

1. _____
_____

2. _____
_____

3. Follow Marsh Drive around the pond.

4. _____
_____

5. _____
_____

6. Pass a little log cabin.

7. _____
_____

> Go west on I-12 to the Denham Springs exit. Turn left at the first light. Follow Marsh Drive as it winds around the pond. Turn left at the stop sign and go about ½ mile. The public hall is the second building on the right after you pass a little log cabin.

DIRECTIONS Write the answer to each of Bettye's mom's questions.

1. "There's the pond, Bettye. What do I do next?"

_____
_____

2. "How far is it from the stop sign to the log cabin, Bettye?"

_____
_____

3. "Where is the hall from the log cabin, Bettye?"

_____
_____

3 Read and Apply

DIRECTIONS Ted and Shoji are cooking dinner for their dads. Write their recipe in step-by-step form.

QUICK AND EASY CHICKEN AND CHINESE VEGETABLES

Heat wok to 375° before adding 2 tablespoons oil. Add 2 boneless chicken breasts cut in bite-size pieces. Stir-fry for 2 to 3 minutes or until chicken is white. Add 1 tablespoon soy sauce. Add one package frozen vegetables and break up any frozen chunks. Cook covered for 3 to 4 minutes. Uncover and stir-fry for an additional 3 to 4 minutes until chicken and vegetables are thoroughly hot.

1. Heat wok to 375°.

2. _____

3. Cut chicken into bite-size pieces.

4. _____

5. _____

6. _____

7. _____

8. Break up frozen chunks.

9. _____

10. _____

11. _____

DIRECTIONS Check Ted and Shoji's progress by writing the number of the step that comes before or after each of the following.

1. before adding soy sauce _____

2. after first stir-fry _____

3. after adding chicken _____

4. before last stir-fry _____

5. after cooking covered 3 to 4 minutes _____

6. after adding vegetables _____

DIRECTIONS Read about listening to take good directions. Then use the tips you've learned to help C. J. write the directions in nine steps.

C. J. was going to his new class-mate's house. Zahir told C. J. to go past the school and turn left onto Phillips Street. He said to go past four stop signs and go left at the next street. From there, C. J. was to turn right onto Marlys Drive where he would see four big buildings in a row on the right. Zahir said to go past the buildings and then make a left turn onto the little street with the one-way sign and go to the fifth house on the left.

C. J. found these directions quite confusing, so he asked Zahir to give them to him slowly and he would write them on the back of his tablet.

"You'll go past the school," said Zahir.

"O.K., I've got that down. What's next?" asked C. J.

Use the tips you've learned about following directions to complete the directions as C. J. wrote them in eight steps.

1. Go past the school

2. _____

   _____

3. _____

4. _____

5. _____

   _____

6. _____

   _____

7. _____

   _____

8. _____

   _____

DIRECTIONS Help C. J. follow his list of directions by writing how you would answer his thoughts.

1. "That's the fourth stop sign. What's next?"

   _____

2. "There's Marlys Drive. What do I do now?"

   _____

3. "There's the one-way sign. Where do I go from here?"

   _____

REMEMBER Follow directions step-by-step and check as you go along.

Long Distance Travelers

Martin hurried to read his mail before running off to his baseball game. He looked for the main idea, knowing he could read the details later. In this lesson, you'll learn to recognize the main idea and details as you read. You'll also read about some long distance travelers.

I hope you can come on Saturday, the 28th at 4p.m. I'm having a party. You'll recognize my driveway as soon as you round the corner of Ashbrook Boulevard and Lenway Drive.

1 KEYS to Main Ideas and Details

Details tell about the main idea.

LEARN The *main idea* is the most important idea in a paragraph: there would be a party. The *details* tell more about the main idea: the party is on Saturday, the 28th at 4:00 at the corner of Ashbrook Boulevard and Lenway Drive.

DIRECTIONS Underline the main idea sentence in each group. Circle the letter before each detail sentence.

a. At school we study many subjects.

b. Science is one of our subjects and math is another.

c. We also study geography and history.

a. Cumulus clouds are puffy.

b. Clouds can have many different shapes.

c. Stratus clouds are rather flat.

DIRECTIONS Read each of the following paragraphs. Underline the main idea sentence. The first one has been done for you.

1. A thesaurus contains synonyms and antonyms for common words. A rhyming dictionary lists words whose ending sounds are the same. Such resource books are used often by poets who need just the right word to complete a thought. <u>A the-saurus and rhyming dictionary are found in the reference section of the library.</u>

2. She was confident she would win. Her act was well rehearsed. She had carefully planned her few props. Janet was anxious, but optimistic about the upcoming class talent show. For the past several months, she had written, rewritten and finally perfected her humorous monologue. Her costume would be completed by this time tomorrow.

3. A word processor can make a simple task of writing a paper. Once the rough draft is typed, sentences or whole paragraphs can be moved to where you want them. Deleting sentences or whole paragraphs is quickly accomplished. Spelling errors are corrected easily without redoing the whole page.

4. The night air stirred softly. The faint lights hovered in the distance. An eerie sound came from the far corner of the field. Jamie was excited about his adventure, but he was also somewhat apprehensive. What if they found out? What if he got there too late? What if the ground hadn't yet thawed sufficiently?

5. He passed the puck and then skated toward the blue line, halting only momentarily for Brian to advance. Then, bursting forward with all his might, he skillfully dodged the defenseman and was instantly in position. Brian passed. He received the puck, dribbled it past his opponent and shot. The winning goal was scored for the Pirates!

Read and Apply

DIRECTIONS As you read this story about some cooperative research, think about the main idea and details within paragraphs.

Mindy and Amit had been friends for years. Their families often went camping together. During these trips, the two of them liked to watch the wild geese migrate north in springtime and south in autumn. It was no wonder that when the time came to do their science project, Amit and Mindy decided to team up and take a closer look at bird migration.

They began their research. Their first stop was the school library. There they checked the card catalogue for information about migration. They found many titles about birds. But what was this? There was lots of information about butterflies.

"Do butterflies migrate?" asked Mindy, surprised.

"I guess they do," said Amit. "That's fascinating! I'd like to read some more about it. How about you?"

"Sure," said Mindy. "We'll still have time to get all the facts about wild geese."

Mindy went off to look up the specific references on monarch butterflies while Amit researched the materials on other types of butterflies. He found that some types of butterflies travel thousands of miles, despite their being so fragile. He read about the painted lady butterfly who travels from North Africa to Iceland and back.

Meanwhile, Mindy quickly became engrossed in the black and bright orange monarch butterflies. She read that the monarch of North America is one of the hardiest travelers, spending the winter near the Gulf of Mexico and then flying north to Canada in the spring.

"Hey, Amit, look at this," she whispered. "It says here that the monarch follows the growth of its favorite food, the milkweed plant. That's the way you follow the smell of pizza!"

"O.K. wise girl! If you're so clever, answer this! How can butterflies possibly protect themselves during such long trips?"

"Easy to answer! I just read it! See, it says here that a butterfly's colors help camouflage it. Then a bird can't have it for dinner."

"Well, I read that so many butterflies migrate in a group that they look like a cloud. I also learned that they occasionally stop to lay their eggs."

"I read that, too, Amit," said Mindy. "Uh-oh, look at the clock. We have to be home in ten minutes. What'll we do?"

"Mindy, I know we'd planned to do our report on the geese, but what do you think of doing it on migrating butterflies? We've got everything we need. Besides, if things go as usual, Mr. Frazier will assign another report next month and one or both of us can do that one on wild geese."

"You're on, Amit, but I get geese for the next one! Let's go!"

DIRECTIONS Read each of the sentences below. Circle MI if it is a main idea sentence in the story. Circle D if it is a detail sentence.

1. We've got everything we need.   MI   D

2. It says here that the monarch follows the growth of its favorite food, the milkweed plant.   MI   D

3. They began their research.   MI   D

4. He found that some types of butterflies travel thousands of miles, despite their being so fragile.   MI   D

5. They found many titles about birds.   MI   D

6. Meanwhile, Mindy quickly became engrossed in the black and bright orange monarch butterflies.   MI   D

7. There they checked the card catalogue for information about migration.   MI   D

8. Mindy and Amit had been friends for years.   MI   D

9. There was lots of information about butterflies.   MI   D

10. He read about the painted lady butterfly who travels from North Africa to Iceland and back.   MI   D

REMEMBER The main idea is explained by the details.

Why Wear Clothing?

Most people of the world wear clothing of some kind, though their reasons for doing so are not always the same. In this lesson, you will read about clothing as you learn to organize information.

1 KEYS to Main Idea, Subtopics, Details

Details explain subtopics while subtopics explain a main idea.

LEARN Information can be sorted into a main idea, subtopics, and details by drawing a *tree diagram*.

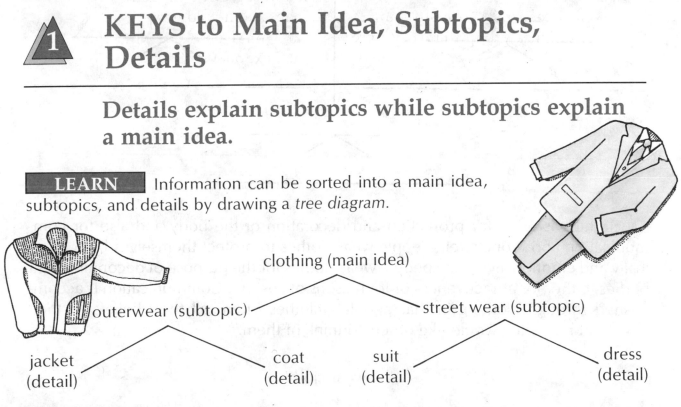

clothing (main idea)

outerwear (subtopic)   street wear (subtopic)

jacket   coat   suit   dress
(detail)   (detail)   (detail)   (detail)

DIRECTIONS Use the word list as you complete the tree diagram to show which methods of fastening clothes are quick and which take longer.

| zipper | button | slowly | snap | quickly | Velcro |

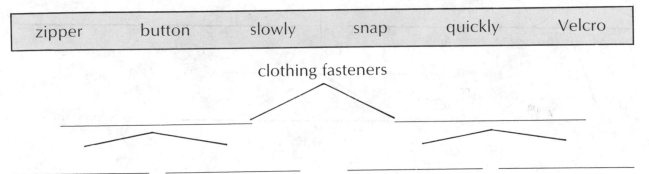

clothing fasteners

Practice With Main Idea, Subtopics, and Details

DIRECTIONS Read the first paragraph. Use the underlined words to complete the tree diagram. Then read the second paragraph and complete the tree diagram.

Clothing includes more than just garments such as trousers or dresses. Ornaments such as bracelets and earrings are part of the clothing of many people, as are accessories such as belts or handbags.

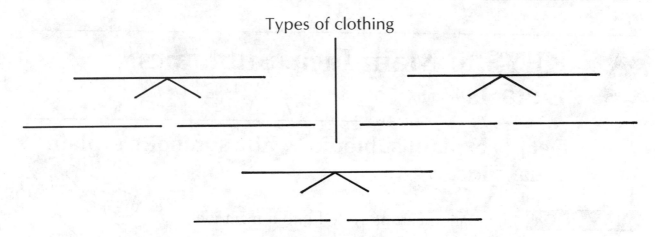

Types of clothing

Clothing is worn for protection and decoration of the body and also for communication about one's self. People wear clothes to protect themselves both physically and emotionally. Many people wear clothes for the purpose of decorating their bodies, either for attractiveness or for reasons of custom. Communication is accomplished through clothing in that people's clothes often tell their beliefs or their wishes of how they would like others to think of them.

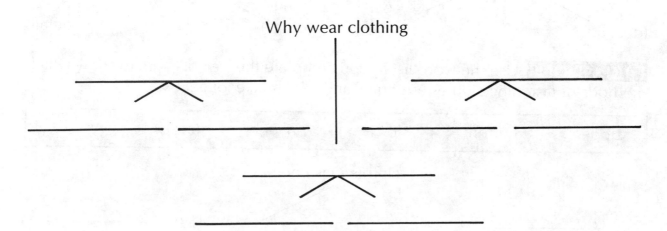

Why wear clothing

Read and Apply

DIRECTIONS Look for the main idea, subtopics, and details in each paragraph as you read how the production of clothing has changed with time.

A. People have probably been wearing clothes for one hundred thousand years, but the creation of clothing has changed drastically over the years. Clothes were handmade in homes and small businesses prior to the introduction of machinery in the late 1700's. Factories then began to produce clothing by using the spinning jenny which could spin threads to make fabrics. A steam-powered loom further increased production as greater quantities of cloth could be manufactured in less time.

B. People use many different materials to make clothing. Some natural fabrics such as cotton and wool from animals have been used for centuries. Man-made fabrics such as nylon and plastic, however, have come to be widely used in the clothing industry since the early 1900's.

C. Man-made fabrics, called synthetics, are created through the combination of chemical compounds or from natural fibers. The use of synthetics has certain advantages over the use of natural fabrics. Many synthetics are less expensive to use and they are stronger.

D. Although common synthetics such as plastic and paper have not been widely used as fabrics for articles of clothing, their use is steadily increasing. The popularity of disposable clothing such as diapers meant a boom in the use of both paper and plastic. The clothing industry has long used plastic for outerwear, and just recently, a new use for paper emerged in what designers hope will be a successful idea, paper wedding gowns.

Complete a tree diagram for each paragraph in the article you just read.

A.

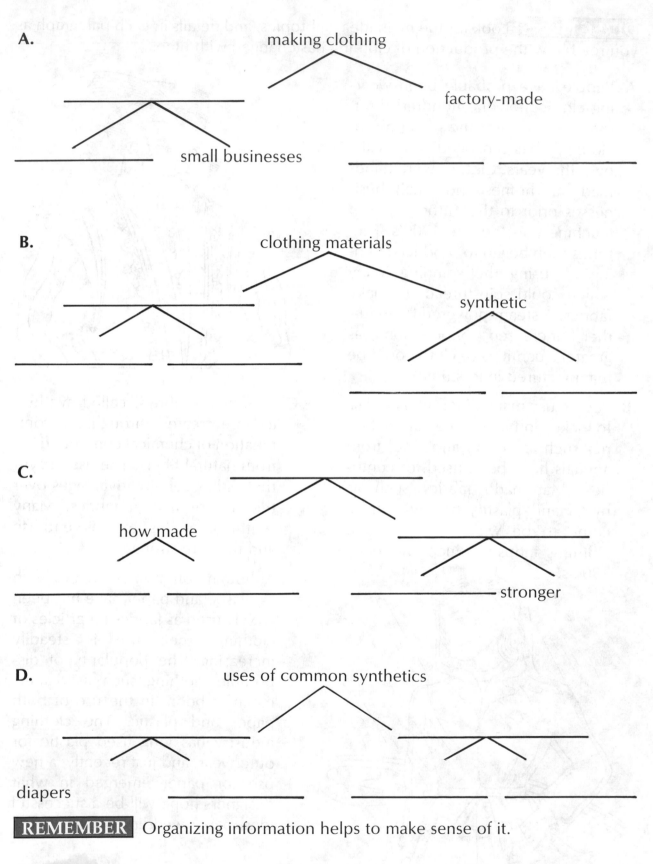

making clothing

factory-made

small businesses

B.

clothing materials

synthetic

C.

how made

stronger

D.

uses of common synthetics

diapers

Organizing information helps to make sense of it.

Roads That Move

Imagine reading a book or article filled with information about a subject totally new to you. In this lesson you will learn to organize information. You'll also learn about "roads that move."

⓵ KEYS to Main Idea, Subtopics, Details

Organizing information helps you see how it all fits together.

EXAMPLE The topic of flowers might be divided into two subtopics. The main idea, flowers, includes the subtopics, annuals and perennials.

I. Flowers
  A. Annuals
  B. Perennials

DIRECTIONS Think about which of the three words in each group below includes the other two words. Write the main idea after Roman Numeral I and the subtopics after the capital letters A and B.

1. North America

  Continents

  South America

I. _____

A. _____

B. _____

2. Atlantic

  Pacific

  Oceans

I. _____

A. _____

B. _____

Practice With Main Idea, Subtopics, Details

DIRECTIONS Details tell more about the subtopic. Look at how the topic of flowers might be organized into specific annuals, which have to be planted every year, and perennials, which sprout new growth each year.

I. Flowers
    A. Annuals
        1. Petunias
        2. Marigolds
    B. Perennials
        1. Tulips
        2. Daffodils

Flowers is the main idea. Annuals and Perennials are the subtopics. Petunias and Marigolds are details that tell more about the subtopic, Annuals. Tulips and Daffodils are details that tell more about the subtopic, Perennials.

DIRECTIONS Look at the countries listed below. Expand the main idea of continents to include some details about North America and South America.

Venezuela
Brazil
United States
Argentina
Peru
Mexico
Columbia
Canada

I. Continents

    A. _____

        1. _____

        2. _____

        3. _____

    B. _____

        1. _____

        2. _____

        3. _____

        4. _____

        5. _____

DIRECTIONS Think about *main idea, subtopics,* and *details* as you read this article about a special kind of road.

What has its head at one end and its mouth at the other? Here are some hints: its head usually begins high up in the mountains, and its mouth empties into the sea. The space between its head, or headwaters, and its mouth may be thousands of miles long and contain millions of tons of water.

The water of a river (Did you guess it?) always seeks the lowest point as it runs down. This lowest point is the sea level. The mouths of all major rivers eventually find their way to the sea.

Rivers begin as trickles from melting snow and spring rains. As the water moves across the land, it cuts into the earth and carries with it tons of soil. This cutting into the land forms canyons, bluffs, and estuaries. Canyons have walls on both sides, whereas a bluff has a rock wall on only one side. Estuaries are canyon-like formations at the river's mouth.

The world's longest river is the Nile. The Nile River begins in central Africa and stretches nearly 4200 miles northward to the Mediterranean Sea. The Amazon River flows for 4000 miles in South America, making it the world's second longest river.

Many people believe the Mississippi River is North America's longest river, but, actually, the Missouri River's 2500-mile length earns the record. The Missouri River is a tributary of the Mississippi, which means it flows into the Mississippi. The point at which the two rivers meet in St. Louis, Missouri is called a confluence.

If one were to follow the Mississippi River, beginning at its mouth at the Gulf of Mexico, to St. Louis, go up

the Missouri to the confluence of the Red Rock River and proceed northward to the headwaters of the Red Rock River, the distance would exceed 3800 miles. This length would rank third longest in the world.

Rivers play a major role in the history of their countries. Large and small cities are often located on river banks. This is because rivers provide transportation for people and goods. Rivers also provide the water necessary for generating electricity. In addition, people look to the rivers of the world for various forms of water recreation.

Considering the size and importance of rivers, it is no wonder that a writer of long ago described rivers as "roads that move and carry us where we wish to go."

DIRECTIONS Choose from the subtopics and details at the right to tell more about each main idea. Write the subtopics and details on the lines.

I. **World's Longest Rivers**

A. _____   Nile River

   1. _____   Nearly 4200 miles long

   2. _____   Second longest river

   3. _____   Amazon River

B. _____   In Africa

   1. _____   In South America

   2. _____   4000 miles long

   3. _____   Longest river

I. **Characteristics of Rivers**

A. _____   Mouths

   1. _____   Cut as they move

   2. _____   Headwaters

B. _____   Bluffs

   1. _____   Estuaries

   2. _____   Ends of rivers

   3. _____   Canyons

REMEMBER Divide main idea into subtopics and subtopics into details.

Otis Cranberry and the Bubble Gum Record

Have you ever dreamed of challenging a world record? In this lesson, you will read about a boy who did. You will learn about sequence, or the order of events in a story.

KEYS to Sequence

Events happen in a specific order.

LEARN When you read a story, you find out what happens at the beginning, middle, and end. The order of events is called *sequence*. Words like *first, next, then, after, before, finally, at last,* and *during* are clues to sequence.

DIRECTIONS Read the beginning of the Otis's story. Then circle the clue words in the sentences below the story.

Otis Cranberry owned a copy of the *Book of Records*. Every day he read it. Some days he read a lot of it. One day Otis had an idea. "I can break one of these records," he told himself. "Then they'll put my name in the *Book of Records,* too."

He thumbed through the book and stopped to read, "Girl blows bubble nineteen-and-one-quarter inches in diameter." That didn't sound so great to Otis.

So Otis took some money from his bank, got his best friend Grover, and off they went to the store. Otis bought a dollar's worth of bubble gum.

1. First Otis read the *Book of Records*.
2. He decided to try to break a record then.
3. Otis and Grover finally bought some bubble gum.

DIRECTIONS Continue reading about Otis. Then read the sentences after the story. Underline the words that tell what happened first.

On the way back home Otis put three whole pieces of bubble gum in his mouth at once and began to chew. He gave Grover a piece, too.

"How are we going to measure the bubble?" Grover wanted to know.

Otis stopped chewing for a moment. He said, "With a yardstick, of course. How else?"

They looked in the book again to check the record. "Girl blows bubble nineteen-and-one-quarter inches in diameter," Grover read aloud. "What's a diameter?"

"From one side to the other," Otis mumbled, still chewing. "As if you were measuring right through the bubble."

His bubble gum was nice and soft now, just right for blowing. He pushed his tongue through it to make sure it would stretch well.

"Stand back," he warned Grover. "Here goes my first try."

Otis took three deep breaths, then began to blow slowly and carefully. A pink bubble began as Grover watched, yardstick in hand. The first bubble burst before it was bigger than an orange. "That was just for practice," Otis told his friend. "I'm just getting warmed up."

Every time Otis blew a new bubble, it was a little bigger than the one before it. Soon he blew a bubble the size of a watermelon. He clamped his lips tightly together and motioned franti-cally to Grover to measure the bubble. Grover held the yardstick up in front of the bubble. His eyes opened wide. "It's nineteen-and-one-quarter inches," he shouted. Otis let the bubble collapse.

"Why did you do that?" Grover demanded.

"I'm not out to *tie* the record," Otis reminded him. "I'm out to break it."

1. After Otis read about a girl who blew a nineteen-and-a-quarter inch bubble, he decided to try to break the record.

2. Before he could blow a good bubble, Otis had to chew the gum until it was soft.

3. He moved the gum to the front of his mouth, then pushed his tongue through it.

4. Otis took three deep breaths, and finally he began to blow a bubble.

5. After Otis blew a bubble that tied the record, he let it collapse.

Read and Apply

DIRECTIONS Think about the sequence of events in the story as you read more about Otis.

Finally Otis decided he was ready for the big try. Slowly he began to blow, and slowly a pink bubble began to grow. Grover stared with round eyes and open mouth as the bubble grew larger and larger.

Suddenly something began to tickle Otis's nose. He knew at once that he was going to have to sneeze. Was it possible that this great moment was about to be spoiled by an itch? Otis kept blowing and the tickle grew worse. He could no longer keep the sneeze back. He clamped his front teeth to the part of the gum still left inside his mouth and sneezed loudly.

What happened next was a shock to both boys. Instead of bursting as they had expected, the huge bubble expanded with a lurch that popped it up around Otis's head. The next moment Otis was looking at his friend Grover from *inside the bubble!* There was plenty of air in there, so he felt no discomfort. When he realized where he was, he grinned—he didn't want to laugh out loud, for fear of breaking the bubble.

Grover was frantic. "Otis, do you think I should break it and set you free?" he yelled.

A faint but definite "No!" came from inside the bubble. "I like it in here."

Word spread quickly throughout the neighborhood. Soon Otis and Grover were surrounded by children of all ages and sizes. A photographer heard about Otis and his head-bubble and came running with her camera. Otis and Grover proudly posed surrounded by the admiring crowd.

After an hour of glory Otis began to feel funny. He was finding it harder to breathe and realized his bubble oxygen had just about been used up. Reluctantly he made a decision. He reached up and gave the enormous bubble a sharp poke. It popped, and Otis sat there with ragged pieces of gum hanging from his face and hair.

His mother was horrified when she saw him. "It will just have to wear off, I guess," she said.

Early the next morning Grover came running over to Otis's house, waving a copy of the morning newspaper.

"We're famous!" he shouted. Otis looked at the paper. There was a photograph of him grinning out from his huge bubble with the words BOY BLOWS BIGGEST BUBBLE IN TOWN printed under it. But because his head had been inside it, Otis figured the *Book of Records* wouldn't let it count.

Later the photographer came to Otis's house and handed him a ten-dol-lar bill. "The newspaper paid me for my photograph," she explained. "Here's a share of it for you."

Otis was pleased. "Well," he said slowly, "it isn't the *Book of Records*, but it's a start."

He reached over and picked up his well-worn book. "Now I can buy a new copy. And I can start making plans for my next try at a world record."

1. **a.** Grover measured the bubble.
   b. Otis started to blow his bubble.
   c. Otis clamped his teeth down on the gum.
   The best order is: a,b,c   b,a,c   b,c,a   c,b,a .

2. **a.** Otis didn't laugh because he was afraid the bubble would break.
   b. Otis sneezed loudly.
   c. The bubble popped up and around Otis's head.
   The best order is: a,c,b   b,c,a   a,b,c   c,a,b .

3. **a.** Grover wondered if he should break the bubble.
   b. A photographer took a picture of Otis and Grover.
   c. Otis's picture appeared in the newspaper.
   The best order is: c,a,b   a,c,b   b,a,c   a,b,c .

4. **a.** Gum was hanging from Otis's face and hair.
   b. Otis gave the bubble a sharp poke.
   c. Otis found it was getting hard to breathe inside the bubble.
   The best order is: b,a,c   c,b,a   a,c,b   c,a,b .

REMEMBER Understanding sequence helps you make sense of a story.

Why Possum's Tail Is Bare

Many years ago, the possum had a long, bushy tail. In this lesson, you will learn about a rabbit's trick as you read a folk tale about why the opossum's tail is bare. You will also learn about sequencing, or how the events in a story happen in a certain order.

1 KEYS to Sequencing

The sequence is the order in which things happen.

LEARN Sequence is the order in which one thing follows another. Sometimes authors use special words to help call attention to the sequence. Words like *first, second, finally, next, then, last, now, beginning,* and *later* help the reader understand the order of a story.

EXAMPLE *Possum combed his tail before he ate break-fast.* The word *before* helps us know that the sequence of events was:

1. Possum combed his tail.
2. Possum ate breakfast.

DIRECTIONS Write the sequence of events in the correct order on the lines.

1. After she saw Possum's tail, the rabbit felt very jealous.

    1. _____

    2. _____

2. The rabbit played a trick on Possum and then she felt better.

    1. _____

    2. _____

Practice With Sequencing

DIRECTIONS Read each part of the story. Look for clue words that help you know what happened before or after another event. Then write *1, 2, 3, 4,* or *5* before each sentence to show the correct sequence of events.

A. There was going to be a dance in the forest, and all the animals were to be summoned. It was Rabbit's duty and privilege to extend the invitations, so first she stopped by Possum's house to ask him whether he would attend. Possum said that he would come only if he could have a specific seat. "I have such a handsome tail!" he bragged. "I just must sit where everyone can see me!"

Rabbit promised to accommodate Possum's request. She also offered to send someone to prepare his tail for the event. Possum was very flattered with her offer and agreed to attend the dance.

Next, Rabbit went off to see Cricket who was an expert hair cutter. Rabbit told Cricket to go the next morning and get Possum's tail ready for the dance. Then she told Cricket exactly what to do.

_____ Possum agreed to go to the dance.

_____ Rabbit offered to send someone to prepare Possum's hair.

_____ Rabbit promised to arrange the special seating.

_____ Rabbit told Cricket how to prepare Possum's tail.

_____ Possum asked for a special seat at the dance.

B. The following morning, Cricket went to Possum's house. "I have instructions to get you ready for the dance, Possum," he said.

Cricket's visit and his announcement delighted Possum, so he stretched himself out and shut his eyes. Then Cricket began his work of grooming Possum's hair. First, he carefully combed the hair. Then he quietly began to clip Possum's hair close to the roots. After he clipped, Cricket wrapped red ribbon around the tail to hold the loose hairs in place. Possum, who was not watching, didn't know what Cricket was doing.

_____ Cricket began to work on Possum's tail.

_____ Possum stretched out and closed his eyes.

_____ Cricket wrapped a red ribbon around Possum's tail.

_____ Cricket clipped the hair on Possum's tail.

_____ Cricket explained why he had come.

Read and Apply

DIRECTIONS Think about the sequence of events as you read what happened when Possum went to the dance.

That evening, Possum went to the place where the dance was to be held. After he got there, he noticed that the best seat in the house was ready for him, just as Rabbit had promised. Then it was Possum's turn to dance and, grinning from ear to ear, he stepped into the middle of the floor.

The drummers began to drum and Possum began to sing, "See my beautiful tail!" Everyone shouted and this pleased Possum, so he danced around the circle again and sang, "See what a fine color my tail is!" Everyone shouted again, and Possum danced around the circle once more. As he danced, he chanted, "See how my tail sweeps the ground so gracefully!"

The animals shouted more loudly than ever and Possum was beside himself with joy. Now, to really show off his fur, he untied the ribbon that held it. Then around and around he danced, singing, "See how fine is the fur on my beautiful tail!"

Suddenly, everybody started to laugh. They laughed so profusely that Possum wondered why they were laughing. He looked around the crowd of guffawing animals. They were laughing at him! Then he looked down at his tail and saw that there was not a hair in sight! It was as bare as the tail of a lizard! Possum was so surprised and embarrassed that he could not utter a word. He slumped to the ground, rolled over, and played dead.

That is why a possum's tail is bare and why the fellow plays dead when taken by surprise.

a. Possum untied the ribbon on his tail.

b. Possum found that the best seat was ready for him.

c. Everyone shouted as Possum sang and danced.

d. The drummers began to play.

e. Possum dropped to the ground and played dead.

f. Possum was surprised and embarrassed.

g. Everyone started to laugh at Possum.

h. Possum looked at his tail.

i. Possum arrived at the dance.

1. _____

2. _____

3. _____

4. _____

5. _____

6. _____

7. _____

8. _____

9. _____

DIRECTIONS Answer the questions about the story.

1. What happened after Cricket clipped Possum's hair on his tail?

_____

_____

2. Where did Rabbit go when he left Possum's house?

_____

_____

3. What did Cricket do first to Possum's tail?

_____

_____

4. What happened after Possum noticed his tail was bare?

_____

_____

REMEMBER A sequence of events tells the order things happen.

I Should Have Known!

Weather reporters make predictions. You predict what Mom or Dad will say before you ask for a special privilege. How is it that predictions are so often correct? In this lesson, you'll learn about making predictions as you read. You'll also read about Leon who, perhaps, *should* have made a prediction!

1 KEYS to Making Predictions

Predictions are "educated guesses" about what will happen.

LEARN   Making a prediction as you read helps you prepare to read on for greater meaning, and often greater enjoyment. You use what you already know and what you've already read to make predictions, or guesses, based on good information.

EXAMPLE   Your past experiences help you predict that Angela is about to be bitten when you read:

Angela glimpsed her hamster's snarl too late.

DIRECTIONS   Read each sentence. Write a sentence predicting what will happen next.

1. Fanny heard a soft thumping sound coming from the dimly lit corner of the basement.

_____

2. Moments after the baseball disappeared, they heard the distinct sound of shattering.

_____

DIRECTIONS Read each paragraph. Circle the letter before the sentence which best predicts what might happen next.

1. Moira unfolded the crumpled note that was sure to answer all her questions. At first glance, she was somewhat puzzled. The scribbling didn't seem at all legible. Then the thought registered that the letters all looked backwards or upside down as if they'd been written in mirror fashion.

    a. Moira throws the note away.

    b. Moira runs to the bathroom mirror.

    c. Moira turns the note sideways.

    d. Moira tosses the note aside, thinking it is unimportant.

2. Rusty knew he was asking for trouble, but he couldn't resist the temptation. Jenny had teased him unmercifully all morning, and she deserved it. He looked up at his sister sitting there at her desk beside the open window. He aimed the nozzle.

    a. Rusty sprays the wilting flowers.

    b. Rusty puts the hose down.

    c. Rusty sprays Jenny through the open window.

    d. Rusty twists the nozzle to shut it off.

3. He sawed slowly at first and then, anxious to be done, moved the blade faster and faster along the guide line he'd drawn. Too late, he remembered Uncle Carl's warning that he should go very slowly at the end of the cut to prevent the wood from splintering.

    a. The wood splinters and he has to start over.

    b. He succeeds in making a neat cut.

    c. His saw bumps into the basement wall.

    d. He hears his friend calling him.

4. The looseness of the G and E keys had been causing trouble for some time now. Mr. Melon had suggested several times that she leave her clarinet at the shop to be repaired before the situation worsened. Gwen hadn't considered how bad it could be until, in the middle of the big concert for the whole school, she heard the piercing shrieks.

    a. The shrieks were from the trumpet section.

    b. Gwen left her clarinet at home.

    c. Gwen's clarinet case wouldn't shut.

    d. Gwen's clarinet keys broke.

Read and Apply

DIRECTIONS Read the story's title and make a prediction about what you think the story is about. Read the first paragraph and make a prediction about what will happen next. Read on and compare your prediction to what actually happens before you make your next prediction.

I Should Have Known!

1. I predict this story will be about _____

Ms. Morgan, the librarian, was always suggesting books and stories for Leon to read. He wanted to be respectful, but most times he managed to ignore her suggestions. He thought he did a pretty good job of faking, however, when she'd mention the stories to him. He usually tried to get her to do all the talking and then he'd excuse himself or change the subject. Leon often wondered if Ms. Morgan had any idea that he didn't follow up on her recommendations. Surely not. She had too many other kids to help. He figured that with her being a teacher, she was interested in him and wanted to help him make good selections. Nonetheless, she usually would hand him the weirdest things like articles on bananas after she noticed he had a banana in his lunch every single day. Then there was the strange story about the handicapped robot. She'd given that one to him after she saw his science project. Ms. Morgan never seemed to give up and today had been no exception.

2. I predict that _____

"I think you'll get a kick out of this story, Leon," she'd said as she laid out a huge volume opened to the Table of Contents. She'd pointed to a story titled "You Haven't Fooled Me!" Leon fully intended to put the book back on the shelf as soon as Ms. Morgan went off to help another student. He pretended to be reading while he waited for her to leave, but it didn't happen the way he'd anticipated.

3. How did your prediction compare to what happened? _____

_____

_____.

4. I predict that _____

_____.

Ms. Morgan lowered herself into the chair beside him. He was caught! Feeling forced, he read the title. He liked anything that suggested trickery. He read the first few paragraphs and found, in spite of himself, that he wanted to continue reading. The story was about a boy who loved movies. The character convincingly pretended to have read lots of books, but actually had not gone beyond the book jackets.

5. How did your prediction compare to what happened? _____

_____.

6. I predict that _____

_____.

"He's read the descriptions on the book jackets and seen the movies," thought Leon in silent admiration. "That's the way I fake out Ms. Morgan. That's pretty neat, except that the sto- ry's title leads me to think that he must get caught. Uh-oh, I think I know why she suggested this story. I should have known!"

7. How did your prediction compare to what happened? _____

_____.

8. Look at your first prediction of what the story would be about. Compare it to the

   story you read. _____

_____.

REMEMBER Read, think, and make a prediction.

What Does This Mean?

You must often think hard to understand what a poem means. In this lesson you will learn to make inferences by using the words of a poem along with your own ideas.

1 KEYS to Making Inferences

Words you read + own ideas = Inference

LEARN   When you read or listen to someone speak, you combine the words with your own ideas to make inferences in order to understand the words.

DIRECTIONS Note the clues in this poem and the "in-the-head" clues. Answer the questions.

Who Do You Think It Is?

Who do you think sprouts a coat of spikes
From top to tail whenever he likes?
(Not a coat to stroke against the grain . . .
Not a pet to pat. That's clear and plain!)
Who puts up quills that stand on end
Till he makes up his mind . . . Are you foe or friend?
Some creatures have shells that close up tight
When dangerous enemies come into sight.
Some use stingers, claws, and bills . . .
But who is this pincushion full of quills?
Who sprouts needles, quick as scat
(When they had been lying down smooth and flat)?
Who plainly shows he's not delighted
When troublesome guests come uninvited?

—Mabel Watts

> My best "In-the-Head" clues were:
>
> 1. animals' ways of protecting themselves.
>
> 2. an animal that is not kept as a pet
>
> 3. an animal that has sharp quills for protection

1. What was Mabel Watts writing about? _____

Practice Making Inferences

2

Combine your own ideas with clues from each poem to complete activities A and B to the right of each poem.

1.   The Secret

We have a secret, just we three,
The robin and I and the sweet cherry-tree;
The bird told the tree and the tree told me,
And nobody knows it but just us three.

But of course the robin knows it best.
Because he built the—I shan't tell the rest;
And laid the four little—something in it—
I'm afraid I shall tell it every minute.

But if the tree and the robin don't peep,
I'll try my best the secret to keep;
Though I know when the little birds fly about
Then the whole secret will be out.

              —Anonymous

A. MAKE AN INFERENCE: What is the secret?

_____

_____

B. MY BEST "IN-THE-HEAD" CLUES WERE:

_____

_____

_____

_____

2.   Waiting

Dreaming of honeycombs to
    share

With her small cubs, a mother
    bear
Sleeps in a snug and snowy lair.
Bees in their drowsy, drifted
    hive
Sip hoarded honey to survive
Until the flowers come alive.
Sleeping beneath the deep
    snow
Seeds of honeyed flowers
    know
When it is time to wake and
    grow.

              —Harry Behn

A. MAKE AN INFERENCE: What are the bear, bees, and seeds waiting for?

_____

B. MY BEST "IN-THE-HEAD" CLUES WERE:

_____

_____

_____

Read and Apply

DIRECTIONS Read these short poems which have been translated by Louis Untermeyer. Use a dictionary for unfamiliar words. Gather clues from the poems and from your head to make inferences. Complete the sentence under each poem.

1. Motto

Look straight at the task
  without dismay—
And if you can do it,
  do it today.

This poem means

_____

_____

_____

_____

2. Short Sermon

To give—and forgive—
Is a good way to live.

This poem means

_____

_____

_____

_____

3. Good Advice

Don't shirk your work
For the sake of a dream;
A fish in a dish
Is worth ten in the stream.

This poem means

_____

_____

_____

_____

4. Day-Dreamer

Too much thought
Too little wrought.

This poem means

_____

_____

_____

_____

DIRECTIONS Read these riddle poems by anonymous poets. Combine clues from each poem with your own ideas. Then complete each inference statement.

1. There's a flower in the garden
    It's just like a cup;
  It's yellow, as yellow as butter,

    And they call it _____ .

2. He used to crawl along the ground
    Then busy spinning he was found
  He hung his cradle on a bough
    And, in it, he is sleeping now.

  The clues I have gathered tell me this poem is about a _____ .

3. I am as black as black can be, but yet I shine.
    My home was deep within the earth, in a dark mine.
  Though black I seem to be, yet I can glow;
    Just put me on a blazing fire and you will know.

  The clues I have gathered tell me the black thing is _____ .

4. First they dress in green,
    Then they change this gown,
  And each one is seen
    In red or gold or brown.

  The clues I have gathered tell me this poem tells about _____ .

5. Riddle me, riddle me, what is that
  Over the head and under the hat?

  The clues I have gathered tell me the answer is _____ .

6. A few still patter as they fall,
  The squirrels did not yet get them all.

  The clues I have gathered tell me the squirrels didn't get all the _____ .

REMEMBER You use "book clues" and "head clues" to make inferences.

Poisonous Snakes

You use your own knowledge each time you read. In this lesson you will learn about using your bank of "head clues" to get the most meaning from your reading. You will also learn about poisonous snakes.

1 KEYS to Making Inferences

Book clues plus clues from your head help you make inferences.

LEARN You make inferences when you put "head clues" or what you already know, together with "book clues" or what you read.

DIRECTIONS Read about poisonous snakes and answer the question. Underline the word clues in the paragraph. List your best "head" clues.

Poisonous snakes are like crocodiles, piranha fish and sharks. They are mostly dangerous in stories. Real snakes don't go looking for trouble. They want to be left alone and they bite their enemies only out of self-defense. After all, they've got something more important to do—catch prey. Some snakes squeeze their prey to death. But poisonous snakes use their poison, or venom, to kill their prey.

Question: What is the meaning of prey? _____

Best "book clues": _____

Best "head clues": _____

Inference I made: _____

Practice With Cause and Effect

DIRECTIONS Read the questions. Think about the questions as you read the story about rattlesnakes. Gather "book clues" and "head clues" to write an answer to each question. List the clues you used.

1. Is the timber rattler a poisonous

snake? _____

Best "book" clues: _____

_____

Best "head" clues: _____

_____

2. Why do you think the timber rattler

is called a pit viper? _____

_____

_____

Best "book" clues: _____

_____

Best "head" clues: _____

_____

3. Where on a rattlesnake's body

would you find its rattles? _____

Best "book" clues: _____

_____

Best "head" clues: _____

_____

Body in a tight coil. Neck in the shape of an S. Tongue waving slowly. Rattle shaking loudly. Every deer, bear, cow, or human knows what these signs mean. Beware! Rattlesnake! Don't go near!

Many snakes twitch their tails when angry, but only a rattler makes noise. Its stack of hard rings rattles when it senses danger. A timber rattler has no trouble finding food, even with its poor sense of hearing and the little light at night when it hunts. Two holes on the side of its head, called pits, sense the body heat of mice, rats, and rabbits. When the rattler is close enough, its long fangs jab like needles. Venom flows through the fangs and into the prey. The snake lets go just as quickly as it struck. The prey may crawl away, but it falls dead in just a few minutes.

DIRECTIONS Read this story about copperhead snakes. Then read each sentence below and circle the word to tell if the statement is true or false. Tell about the clues you used to make your inferences.

Copperheads are not as poisonous as rattlers and almost never kill anyone. They use their forked tongues to smell you, not to harm you. Like all poisonous snakes, the beautiful copperhead bites with its fangs. Copperheads are pit vipers that often hunt at night.

Copperheads live in rocky places in the East. Their coppery pattern hides them among dead leaves. A baby copperhead may stay hidden in leaves but still find plenty to eat. The tip of the baby's tail is bright yellow. When it twitches, it looks like a wiggling worm which often acts as a perfect lure for hungry toads.

1. A copperhead snake will bite people.   true   false

My best clues were: _____

2. Copperhead snakes are usually found in California.   true   false

My best clues were: _____

3. The copperhead is more dangerous than a rattlesnake.   true   false

My best clues were: _____

4. A baby copperhead uses its tail to capture toads.   true   false

My best clues were: _____

5. A copperhead's pits tell it when its prey is near.   true   false

My best clues were: _____

DIRECTIONS Read the questions below the article about the cottonmouth snake. Then, as you read the article, think about searching for answers to the questions.

One look at that wide open mouth tells you how this snake got its name. The cottonmouth's other name, water moccasin, tells you that it lives in or near the water. The cottonmouth is North America's only poisonous water snake. It is found only in the Southeast, the Mississippi Valley and Texas. Like the harmless water snakes, it catches frogs and fish. It also eats birds and mammals.

Some people confuse harmless water snakes with cottonmouths. Their markings may look alike, but the snakes don't act alike. If you surprise a harmless water snake close up, it will glide into the water and hide. But if you surprise a cottonmouth close up, it may have a little surprise for you! It will throw its head back and open its mouth wide. That white skin should tell you clearly—dangerous snake! Stay away!

DIRECTIONS Now re-read each question, think, and write your answer.

1. Why would you be unlikely to find a cottonmouth living in the states of Maine or Vermont? _____

2. Do travelers in desert areas need to watch out for the cottonmouth snake? _____ Why? _____

3. How do you think the cottonmouth snake got its name? _____

_____

What makes you think so? _____

4. Is a water snake that is not a cottonmouth dangerous? _____
How do you know? _____

REMEMBER Head clues + book clues = inference

Touring Mammoth Cave

Can you imagine what it would be like to explore the land beneath the earth's surface? In this lesson, you will learn about Mammoth Cave, which is the longest cave system in the world. You will also learn to tell the difference between facts and opinions.

1 KEYS to Facts and Opinions

A fact is true, but an opinion is someone's feeling.

LEARN A fact tells something that is true and can be checked. An opinion tells how a person feels about something, although others may disagree. Since an opinion tells what a person believes is true, it cannot be proven right or wrong. Words like *believe, feel, think, seem,* and *probably* are clues that a statement is an opinion.

EXAMPLE If someone tells you that *Mammoth Cave is located in the state of Kentucky,* you can check the fact to see if it is true. If someone tells you that *the best time to visit Mammoth Cave is in the winter,* you cannot prove that their opinion is right or wrong.

DIRECTIONS Read each sentence. Put an X in the appropriate column to tell if the statement is a fact or an opinion.

	Fact	Opinion
1. Mammoth Cave is more fun than Carlsbad Caverns.	_____	_____
2. The Echo River is the best part of the tour.	_____	_____
3. You see things in underground caves that you cannot see above ground.	_____	_____
4. There are underground streams in many caves.	_____	_____

Practice With Facts and Opinions

2

DIRECTIONS Read each statement. Write *fact* on the line if the statement can be proven. Write *opinion* if the statement tells what someone thinks is true.

_____ 1. Mammoth Cave is located in southern Kentucky.

_____ 2. It is too far to travel to Mammoth Cave if you live outside of Kentucky.

_____ 3. Visitors to Mammoth Cave should spend more than one day touring it.

_____ 4. Approximately 300,000 tourists visit Mammoth Cave each year.

_____ 5. If you dislike heights, you probably would not enjoy the Mammoth Cave tour.

_____ 6. Mammoth Cave is open all year.

_____ 7. Mammoth Cave was formed by the movement of water over a period of many years.

_____ 8. It is easy to see how places like Giant's Coffin and Fat Man's Misery were named.

_____ 9. Mammoth Cave has the most beautiful rock formations in the world.

_____ 10. Long ago, tourists had to carry lanterns in the cave to see where they were going.

_____ 11. Mammoth Cave has been a popular tourist attraction for more than 100 years.

_____ 12. Mammoth Cave is a National Park.

DIRECTIONS Look for statements of fact and opinion as you read more about Mammoth Cave.

Mammoth Cave is open year round. However, summer is the best time to go because there are five guided tours through the cave. Not all of the tours are offered during the winter season. The tours vary in length from three quarters of a mile to seven miles. It usually takes about one hour to cover each mile of a tour. A person really has to like caves to spend seven hours in one.

The Historic Trip is one of the easiest of all the tours. It is a mile-and-a-half walk that is offered year round. It begins and ends at the Historic Entrance. This is the only natural entrance into the cave. The other entrances are probably not as interesting because they are all man-made. Indians used the cave's natural entrance long before the European explorers came to America. There is evidence that Indians lived in the cave. One of the best liked sights on the Historic Trip seems to be a two-thousand-

year-old mummy found in the cave. It is displayed in a glass case along with other Indian remains. Many people stop to photograph this attraction.

DIRECTIONS Circle the number before each fact. Mark an X on the number before each opinion.

1. Mammoth Cave is open year round.

2. Summer is the best time to visit Mammoth Cave.

3. Not all of the tours are offered in the winter.

4. Tours usually take an hour for each mile.

5. Many people photograph the mummy case.

Read about some special features of Mammoth Cave. Note that each sentence has a number before it. Identify the facts and opinions by writing the numbers on the appropriate lines below.

(1) One of Mammoth Cave's largest rooms is called the Rotunda. (2) Visitors say it is the room with the most interesting history. (3) During the War of 1812, special minerals were mined from the rotunda. (4) They were used to make gunpowder for the American Army.

(5) There are other parts of Mammoth Cave which visitors frequently stop to see. (6) One of these is called Booth's Amphitheater. (7) An actor named Edwin Booth thought this rock formation presented a perfect stage. (8) One day, he stood on the largest rock in the room and repeated lines from a famous play.

(9) Another sight in Mammoth Cave, that is a "must-see", is called Martha Washington's statue. (10) It was probably named this because many people believe that the rock formation looks just like pictures of our first president's wife.

(11) One cave attraction that might seem a little scary to some visitors is called the Giant's Coffin. (12) It is a big limestone block in the shape of a casket. (13) A sight that is not so frightening, though, is a glass tank which displays some blindfish and crayfish taken from streams inside the cave. (14) Because they are blind and have no color in their bodies, these fish probably look strange to many visitors.

FACTS: _____ _____ _____

_____ _____ _____

_____ _____

OPINIONS: _____ _____ _____

_____ _____ _____

DIRECTIONS Write three facts you learned about Mammoth Cave. Write three of your own opinions about Mammoth Cave.

FACTS

1. _____

2. _____

3. _____

OPINIONS

1. _____

2. _____

3. _____

REMEMBER A fact can be proven, while an opinion cannot.

Flying Discs

The flying disc, more commonly known by the manufacturer's name of Frisbee, is a common sight on beaches and playgrounds. In this lesson, you'll read about the game of Frisbee as you study facts and opinions.

KEYS to Facts and Opinions

An opinion cannot be proven like a fact can.

EXAMPLE A fact is a statement about something that actually happened and can be checked:

In 1980, Alan Bonopane set a record for Frisbee throwing at 74 miles an hour.

An opinion tells what someone thinks or believes, but it cannot be proven. People can have different opinions about the same thing:

It would be difficult to break the Frisbee throwing record.

Words like *thought, might, believe, feel, think, seem,* and *probably* are clues that a statement is an opinion.

DIRECTIONS Write *F* on the line before the fact in each pair of sentences. Write *O* before each opinion.

_____ **a.** The world's record for the longest Frisbee throw is 550.8 feet.

_____ **b.** The record of 13.56 seconds isn't very long for a Frisbee to be in the air.

_____ **a.** It is more fun to play Frisbee outside than indoors.

_____ **b.** The indoor distance record is less than the outdoor record.

_____ **a.** Some think that Frisbee throwing should be an Olympic sport.

_____ **b.** Frisbee competitions began in 1957.

② Practice With Facts and Opinions

DIRECTIONS Willie Throwit has been asked to interview Fritz Bee, a champion Frisbee player who is in town for a tournament. While preparing his interview questions, Willie needs to make sure that he gets facts about the game of Frisbee as well as Mr. Bee's opinions about the sport. Decide whether Mr. Bee's *answer* to each question below will be a fact or an opinion. Circle *F* for *fact* or *O* for *opinion*.

1. When was the Frisbee invented?   F   O

2. What do you like best about playing Frisbee?   F   O

3. Which is harder—throwing a Frisbee or catching one?   F   O

4. Where will the next Frisbee contest be held?   F   O

5. Is Frisbee a dangerous sport?   F   O

6. Is Frisbee an Olympic sport?   F   O

7. What equipment do you need for a game of Frisbee?   F   O

8. How do you make a Frisbee curve to the right?   F   O

9. What is the record for the longest Frisbee throw?   F   O

10. Who is the world Frisbee champion?   F   O

11. Why do you think Frisbee is so popular?   F   O

12. Where is the best place to play Frisbee?   F   O

13. What's the hardest Frisbee throw to learn?   F   O

14. Do Frisbees travel farther indoors or outdoors?   F   O

15. What is your favorite Frisbee trick?   F   O

16. What's the record for a Frisbee's time in the air?   F   O

17. What do you think of team Frisbee?   F   O

DIRECTIONS When Willie asked Mr. Bee to explain a game called "Ultimate Frisbee," it was hard for Mr. Bee to stick to the facts of the game without including his opinions. Underline the seven opinion statements Mr. Bee included in his explanation.

The game of "Ultimate Frisbee" was invented by a group of high school students in New Jersey in the late 1960's. "Ultimate," as it is often nicknamed, is a team sport. It is more fun than just tossing and catching a Frisbee with friends.

Ultimate Frisbee seems to resemble a combination of football and soccer. Two teams of seven players play on a field that is 60 yards long and 40 yards wide with two 30-yard end zones. The object is to pass the disc from player to player from one end of the field to the other. You should be in good physical condition if you intend to play an entire game without feeling exhausted.

The rules of Ultimate Frisbee are easier than those of other sports. You cannot walk with the Frisbee. If you catch the disc while running, you're allowed only two steps forward before you must pass it. Another rule is that defensive players may not bump into other players. Some feel this rule should be changed. A team keeps control of the Frisbee as long as it is completing passes, or until a player drops the Frisbee, throws it out of bounds, or allows the other team to get it.

If you enjoy teamwork and tough competition, Ultimate Frisbee will probably become one of your favorite pastimes. You'll want to practice your catching and throwing skills before playing Ultimate Frisbee, though, since you'll want to "carry your load" for your team.

Look for some statements of fact and opinion as you read the article Willie wrote for the school newspaper. Write them below.

To throw a Frisbee correctly, you must flick it with a sharp snap of your wrist. For many first-time Frisbee throwers, this is probably not as easy as it sounds. If you do not keep your wrist stiff, the Frisbee just wobbles around in the air and crashes to the ground. Some people should be congratulated for getting a Frisbee to sail across the yard without hitting anyone.

Experienced Frisbee players can throw a disc many different ways. These include throwing backhand, sidearm, underhand, overhand, under the leg, and behind the back. There are also a number of ways to catch a Frisbee, such as with one hand, two hands, behind the back, under the leg, between the legs, or standing on one foot. Dogs are known for their Frisbee catching prowess.

Once you become more familiar with how to throw and catch a Frisbee, you can move on to more advanced maneuvers. You'll probably need a lot of practice, though, since learning to make a Frisbee dip and rise through the air takes a lot of experience. Fortunately, you do not need to know how to do these things to enjoy the game.

FACT: _____

_____

FACT: _____

_____

OPINION: _____

_____

_____

OPINION: _____

_____

DIRECTIONS Change each fact to an opinion. One is done for you.

1. I can throw a frisbee backhand.
   It is easy to throw a frisbee
   _____
   backhand.
   _____

2. You must keep a stiff wrist to throw a frisbee.
   _____
   _____

3. My dog plays frisbee.
   _____
   _____

4. I can play a whole game of frisbee without getting too tired.
   _____
   _____

REMEMBER If it can be proven, it's a fact!

Lanterns in the Dark

You won't need a flashlight to find one of the most popular nighttime insects. The firefly, or lightning bug, carries its own light around, turning it off and on in a regular pattern. In this lesson, you will learn more about these little "lanterns" that can light up an entire field, lawn, or woods. You will learn that when one event makes another event happen, there is a cause and effect relationship.

 ## KEYS to Cause and Effect

When one thing happens, it can cause something else to happen.

LEARN   To figure out the cause and effect, ask yourself these two questions: 1. What happened? (effect) 2. Why did it happen? (cause) Words like *because, since, so,* and *that is why* are signal words that tell there is probably a cause and effect relationship. The lightning bugs were easy to see because of their flashing yellow lights. *What happened?* Lightning bugs were easy to see. This is the *effect. Why did it happen?* Because of their flashing yellow lights. This is the *cause.*

DIRECTIONS Read each sentence. Write the words that tell the *effect.* Write the words that tell the *cause.*

1. We put the lightning bugs in a jar so they couldn't get away.

EFFECT: _____

CAUSE: _____

2. It is hard to catch fireflies during the day because they only light up at night.

EFFECT: _____

CAUSE: _____

2 Practice With Cause and Effect

DIRECTIONS Read about fireflies. Then, before each cause, write the letter of its effect.

It is easy to catch fireflies because they move slowly and give themselves away with their flash of light. In the daytime, a firefly is disappointing, since it's such a drab creature. When it performs its amazing act of lighting up at night, however, it ceases to be drab. Instead, it becomes spectacular.

There are several common kinds of fireflies, but you probably won't see all of them at the same time. This is because they hatch at different times during the summer. The ones you find in your area may fly only between dusk and sunset. Others may be active only for a few weeks in early summer. Lightning bugs stay close to the ground, and the males flash a single yellow light about every six seconds. Hot summer nights are a good time to see lightning bugs, because they flash more often in hot weather. Another interesting fact is that lightning bugs fly in an up and down pattern. Since they always flash on the upswing, it's easy to tell whether it is taking off or landing.

Since young lightning bugs stay on the ground, they are sometimes called "glowworms." There's a saying that seeing a glowworm crossing your path will cause brilliant success in whatever you do that day.

EFFECT

a. It ceases to be drab

b. You'll have success

c. It is easy to catch lightning bugs

d. Fireflies are disappointing to look at in the daytime

e. You won't see all the different fireflies at one time

f. Hot summer nights are a good time to see lightning bugs

g. You can tell whether a lightning bug is taking off or landing

h. Young lightning bugs are called "glowworms"

CAUSE

_____ **1.** because they are so drab.

_____ **2.** since they stay on the ground.

_____ **3.** because they flash on the upswing.

_____ **4.** because they move so slowly.

_____ **5.** because they flash more often in hot weather.

_____ **6.** because they hatch at different times during the summer.

_____ **7.** if a glowworm crosses your path.

_____ **8.** when it lights up at night.

DIRECTIONS Think about cause and effect as you read more about fireflies.

The firefly, or lightning bug, is not a fly, nor is it a bug. It is a beetle with two wing cases on its back. These wings are lifted up and out of the way of a second pair of wings when the firefly flies.

There are fireflies in many parts of the world. Some shine much more brightly than others. In some areas, because their light is so bright, people keep fireflies in a glass bottle and use them for a lantern or lamp to read by. In Thailand and Burma, thousands of fireflies gather on certain trees, and together they flash their lights on and off. This causes many people to believe that they are watching lightning coming from the trees.

A firefly seems to glow constantly and flash briefly when held in the hand. If it has been injured, however, it will not flash normally. Instead, it will flash almost constantly and look as though its regulator is out of order.

The firefly's light does not help it see where it is going since it is located in the rear part of its body. The light is certainly no protection against enemies, because the light is easier to see in the dark. In fact, because some frogs have eaten so many lightning bugs, their stomachs shine as if they had swallowed a whole light bulb!

You may wonder then, why the firefly lights up. Scientists believe that fireflies light up so they can find a mate. Unlike most insects, fireflies are attracted by light rather than by the smell or sound of other fireflies. The female firefly stays in the grass and answers the male firefly's light with a flash she turns on two seconds after she sees the male's signal. Because male fireflies watch for lights on the ground, you might be able to attract one by putting a flashlight on the ground.

1. Lightning bugs do not have protection from enemies because
   a. the light is in the rear part of their body.
   b. the light makes the lightning bugs easier to see.
   c. lightning bugs fly in the air.

2. In some areas, people keep fireflies in a glass bottle so the fireflies
   a. make a bright light for reading.
   b. do not get away.
   c. will live longer.

3. A lightning bug may look as though its generator isn't working because
   a. it is injured.
   b. it is lost.
   c. it is hungry.

4. Fireflies light up so
   a. frogs can see them.
   b. they can see where they are going.
   c. they can attract a mate.

5. Some frogs have stomachs that shine as if they had swallowed a light bulb because
   a. they are trying to attract lightning bugs.
   b. they have eaten so many lightning bugs.
   c. they are trying to light up the dark pond.

6. Because some fireflies gather in trees and flash their lights on and off at the same time, many people think
   a. they are seeing lightning.
   b. the lightning bugs are sending them a message.
   c. they will have good luck.

7. A lightning bug sometimes flashes almost constantly because
   a. it is scared.
   b. it has been injured.
   c. it is searching for food.

REMEMBER The effect tells what happened and the cause tells why.

Animal Superstitions

Long ago, when people were sick, in trouble, or wanted more power, they turned to animals for help. In this lesson, you will read about unusual things people thought animals could do. You will learn about cause and effect.

1 KEYS to Cause and Effect

The cause makes the effect happen.

LEARN The reason why something happens is called the *cause*. The thing that happens is called the *effect*.

EXAMPLE People of long ago placed spider webs on cuts so the bleeding would stop.

The *cause* is *so that the bleeding would stop*. The *effect* is *people placed spider webs on cuts*. Words like *because*, *so*, and *this is why* often signal the beginning of a cause statement.

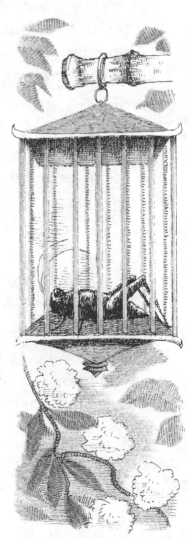

DIRECTIONS Circle the word that tells whether the underlined part of the sentence is the cause or the effect.

1. Some people carry a rabbit's foot, because they believe it will bring them good luck.

    cause   effect

2. Crickets were once so valued for their singing that they were kept in cages and carefully cared for.

    cause   effect

3. Groundhogs are in popular demand on February 2, because people believe they predict how much more winter weather there will be.

    cause   effect

DIRECTIONS Read each paragraph below. Draw one line under the words that tell a cause. Draw two lines under the words that tell an effect.

1. The Chinese people built "owl corners" on the roofs of their homes, because they thought these owl-shaped decorations would protect their buildings from fire.

2. During times when there was a great lack of food and many people were starving, the Ainu people of Japan nailed owls carved from wood to their houses. This was because wooden owls were supposed to end people's bad luck and bring them good fortune.

3. In England, some people ate owl eggs. They did this because they hoped that the eggs would help them see in the dark, as owls do.

4. Cherokee Indians bathed their children's eyes with water and owl feathers so the children would receive the owl's power to stay awake at night.

5. It was once believed that owl soup would make a cough go away. This is why the soup was fed to a person suffering from whooping cough.

6. In Italy, people feared the hooting call of the owl, because they thought it meant someone would develop tonsil trouble.

7. Some people believe it is a good idea to place an owl feather under the pillow of a sleeping person so they will have a peaceful rest.

Read and Apply

DIRECTIONS Look for cause and effect relationships as you read about some animal superstitions.

There are many legends about animals. The wolf is a popular animal in these stories. Some Native American Indian tribes thought that if someone killed a wolf, two bad things would happen. First, the weapon they used to kill the wolf would never work right again. Second, the animals would disappear from the forest.

An English writer in the fifteenth century gave some strange advice about wolves. He told people to wrap wolfskin around their feet when they were traveling. He believed that the wolfskin would make it easier for people to travel long distances. The same writer claimed that people should eat wolfskin so that they would not have nightmares.

Animal cures for heart trouble were also very popular in the past. Deer blood was used by some people to treat heart trouble. This cure probably came from the old belief that the deer has a strong heart. In another country, a common cure for heart trouble was to spread powdered toadskin on the chest of the ill person.

The people of ancient China thought the blood and skin of snakes would improve eyesight and cure skin problems. This was probably because snakes have such smooth skin and appear to see well.

In some countries, ground up tiger bones were used to help heal some-one with a broken bone. A paste of powdered bones was applied to the area around the injury. Tiger bones were used because tigers are very strong animals.

Some animal cures were just plain silly. Sometimes they were dangerous, because they were harmful to the people who tried them. These cures were probably even worse for the animals used for the cures, since the animals often were injured or killed.

Finish each numbered sentence below by writing one of the causes on the line.

Causes: **a.** because animals would disappear from the forest.
b. because tigers are very strong animals.
c. so they would not have nightmares.
d. because they may be harmful to people who try them.
e. because they believed deer had strong hearts.

1. A paste of ground up tiger bones was used to help a person with broken bones

_____

2. Animal cures are dangerous _____

_____

3. One writer suggested that people eat wolfskin _____

_____

4. Some Indian tribes thought wolves should not be killed _____

_____

5. Heart trouble was treated with deer blood _____

_____

DIRECTIONS Read each statement and find a similar one in the story. Tell if the idea is told as a cause or effect. Circle C for cause or *E* for effect.

1. Weapons may never work right again.   C   E
2. Wolfskin was wrapped around the feet.   C   E
3. Tigers are strong animals.   C   E
4. Animals lost their lives.   C   E
5. Powdered toadskin was put on ill people's chests.   C   E
6. People could travel long distances.   C   E
7. Someone killed a wolf.   C   E
8. Snakes have smooth skin and can see well.   C   E
9. People should eat wolfskin.   C   E

REMEMBER An effect happens when there's a cause.

Sports Inventions

What kinds of sporting equipment are in store for the future? Will we see shoes with springs that let players leap high in the air, or a robot umpire that makes no mistakes? These ideas may sound strange to you now, but they may become the sports equipment of the future. In this lesson, you'll read about new sports inventions as you learn about cause and effect relationships.

1 KEYS to Cause and Effect

The cause tells why, and the effect tells what happened.

LEARN   There may be a cause and effect relationship even though a writer does not use clue words.

It rained hard today. The softball game had to be postponed.

The *effect* is that *the softball game had to be postponed*. The *cause* is that *it rained hard today*.

DIRECTIONS In each pair of sentences, write *C* before the *cause*. Write *E* before the sentence that contains the *effect*.

1. _____ The sun was in my eyes.

   _____ I couldn't see well enough to catch the ball.

2. _____ The score was tied at the end of last night's baseball game.

   _____ It was necessary to play an extra inning.

3. _____ She should be well prepared for the swim meet on Saturday.

   _____ Jessica has been swimming practice laps each day.

Practice With Cause and Effect

DIRECTIONS Look for cause and effect relationships as you read about new kinds of sports equipment.

Although padding protects players from many injuries in body-contact sports, it doesn't prevent all broken bones and bruises. The impact of players crashing into one another can be a powerful force. Therefore, manufacturers are continually seeking to improve sports equipment.

Shoulder pads, a must in contact sports, are now available in plastic with ultralightweight foam. The foam is tightly packed for greater absorption of impact. In addition, the pieces are assembled in layers to provide greater comfort and freedom of movement.

The design of headgear, another necessity for a football or hockey player, is also undergoing changes. A lining of protective pads can now be inserted or removed to allow adjustments for different sized heads.

The new equipment designs were field-tested by college squads before being marketed in stores. The new equipment is now available for everyone from children to professional players.

DIRECTIONS Choose from the list of causes below to complete each sentence. Write the cause on the line.

Causes

a. players are sometimes injured.

b. check the ability to protect players.

c. the impact is absorbed.

d. custom-fit headgear is important.

1. Manufacturers seek to improve equipment, because _____

_____

2. Foam is tightly packed so _____

_____

3. Helmets have adjustable padding, since _____

_____

4. New pieces of equipment were tested before being sold, in order to _____

_____

Read and Apply

DIRECTIONS Read about new inventions in baseball equipment. Then answer the questions.

Baseball players in the past have had to break in their new gloves, but current designs can make the stiff glove problem a thing of the past. A softer and more flexible glove is now available. It has small creases or dimples in the palm to allow a player to easily pocket the ball. Some players feel the ball is less likely to spin out of this softer glove.

Fumbling a ball when blinded by the sun is no joy for any player. A new glove design has colored plastic webbing which is supposed to shield the eyes. This "sunglasses-glove" has not yet passed the test, however. It has to be held up in front of the face and the fingers block a player's vision.

Manufacturers are not displeased when athletes say a new invention isn't quite right. On the contrary, players' opinions are encouraged. Such helpful criticism assists designers of sports equipment to continually improve their products.

1. What brought about the attempt to develop a special glove for shading the eyes?

_____

_____

2. What effect do athletes' comments on new equipment have? _____

_____

3. Why is a softer glove desirable? _____

_____

Read about runners' needs. Then circle the best answer for each question below.

Running, a popular sport today, has inventors busy trying to design better equipment. Runners need to keep their legs and leg muscles fit. They warm up by stretching their legs to keep the muscles from being injured by tightness. The concern of runners that leg muscles stay warmed and flexed right up to the start of a race led inventors to create tights that heat the sweat and hold the heat in.

Aside from the importance of healthy legs, a runner needs good footgear that cushions the feet from the steady impact of running. Sports equipment designers have recognized this need by providing special shoes with removable pads. Runners can select the padding that is most comfortable as well as most appropriate for different running surfaces. A soft red pad is suggested for hard surfaces, a gray pad for regular surfaces, and a harder blue pad for softer running areas.

Keeping in good shape and using special equipment may help many runners feel the success of finishing a race or just running for good health.

1. Why do runners need good shoes?
   a. to go fast and win
   b. to cushion the feet
   c. to warm the leg muscles

3. What happened when inventors recognized a runner's need to maintain warmth in leg muscles?
   a. They ignored the need.
   b. They made special tights.
   c. They improved the shoes.

2. What happens if a runner's leg muscles are cold and tight?
   a. They are flexible.
   b. They sweat.
   c. They can be injured.

4. Why did inventors seek to provide better running equipment?
   a. Running is a difficult sport.
   b. Runners need new legs.
   c. Running is a popular sport.

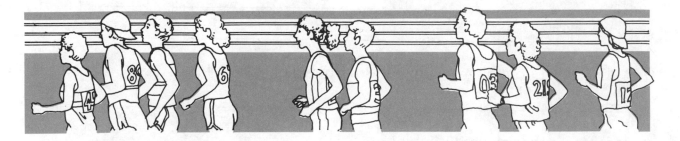

REMEMBER "What happened" is the effect and "why" is the cause.

Special Olympics

"Let me win, but if I cannot win, let me be brave in the attempt." In this lesson, you'll learn about likenesses and differences as you read about a special athletic event with a special oath.

1 KEYS to Comparing and Contrasting

Things can be alike or different or alike *and* different.

LEARN *Contrasting* two things or ideas shows how they differ. *Comparing* may show how two things are similar *or* how they are similar, yet also different.

EXAMPLE
Contrasting: Stephen enjoys swimming, but Marie doesn't.

Comparing: Paula and Ryan are runners. Paula will enter the Olympic Games and Ryan will enter the Special Olympics for mentally handicapped persons.

Stephen's and Marie's interests are different. Paula and Ryan are alike in being runners, but Ryan will participate in different Olympic games from Paula.

DIRECTIONS Write *1* before each sentence that shows a *contrast*. Write *2* before each sentence that shows a *comparison*.

_____ **1.** Marcie and Matthew are competing for the blue ribbon in the Special Olympics.

_____ **2.** Rob is running the relay, and Scott will swim the 100-meter freestyle.

_____ **3.** Harry and Rachel ran the 400-meter, but Harry didn't run the 220.

_____ **4.** The International Summer Special Olympics, like the Olympic Games, are held every four years.

2 Practice Comparing and Contrasting

DIRECTIONS Read each paragraph and complete the sentences.

1. The first Olympic Summer Games were held in Athens, Greece in 1896. The first International Summer Special Olympics Games were held in Chicago, Illinois in 1968.

   a. Contrast: A difference is that _____

   _____.

   b. Compare: A likeness is that _____

   _____.

   The games are both alike and different because_____

   _____.

2. The Olympic Games are international games and are held all over the world. The Special Olympics, held in the United States, involve over 70 countries and all 50 of the United States, as well as the District of Columbia, American Samoa, Guam and the Virgin Islands.

   a. Contrast: A difference is that _____

   _____.

   b. Compare: A likeness is that _____

   _____.

   The games are both alike and different because_____

   _____.

3. Participation in an event in the Special Olympics is more important than winning. Contestants in the Olympic Games compete for medals, while all Special Olympics contestants win a medal or ribbon.

   a. Contrast: A difference is that _____

   _____.

   b. Compare: A likeness is that _____

   _____.

   The games are both alike and different_____

   _____.

DIRECTIONS Read about the Special Olympics.

In 1968, the Joseph P. Kennedy Foundation initiated Special Olympics for mentally retarded individuals from the age of eight to eighty. Currently, more than a million Special Olympians participate in year-round games.

The Special Olympics program is patterned after the well-known Olympic Games, but the emphasis is decidedly different, since winning is not the primary purpose. The goals of the program are to encourage and provide year-round training and competition in athletic events for mentally handicapped children and adults. The physical fitness gained by consistent training, the good feeling of participating, the opportunity to form friendships, and the expressions of courage and good sportsmanship are also very important goals.

In Special Olympics competition, athletes are grouped by ability to participate. Neither a contestant's score nor the outcome of an event is as important as the fact that a special athlete succeeds in crossing the finish line or completing an event. All contestants serve as models to show what can be achieved in spite of any handicap. The Special Olympics symbol of figures resembling people on a globe-like ball represents world-wide winners.

Every two years there is an International Summer or Winter Special Olympics Games which last a full week. Special Olympians who enter the International games qualify by being medal winners in their State or National Games. Twenty-two sports are represented with track and field, basketball, soccer, and swimming being popular events.

As in the Olympic Games, the opening ceremonies of the International Special Olympics are impressive, colorful, and inspirational. Some similar traditions to those of the Olympic Games are seen. The athletes, sporting their identifying flags, march into the stadium in alphabetical order by state or country with Greece in the lead. The games are declared open and drums roll. Then some changes in traditions of the Olympic Games are apparent as the Special Olympics flag is hoisted and thousands of balloons are released in the air.

The dramatic tradition of the lighted Olympic torch being relayed by athletes is also a spectacular part of the opening ceremonies in Special Olympics. The oath, "Let me win, but if I cannot win, let me be brave in the attempt," is recited by all contestants at the start of the games.

DIRECTIONS Read each sentence about the Olympic Games. Then find and underline in the article you just read, some words that show a comparison or contrast to the Olympic Games. Write a comparing or contrasting statement in your own words. The first one is done for you.

1. Hundreds of doves are released during opening ceremonies of the Olympic Games.

    Contrast: Thousands of balloons are released during opening ceremonies in the Special Olympics.

2. The Olympics Games were begun to encourage peace and friendship in the world and also to promote athletics for non-professionals.

    Compare for likeness *and* difference: _____

    _____

    _____

3. The Olympic Games are open to athletes of any age.

    Contrast: _____

    _____

    _____

    _____

4. Entrants in the Olympic Games qualify by gaining high scores or winning in special selection trials.

    Compare for likeness: _____

    _____

    _____

    _____

REMEMBER Comparing and contrasting show likenesses and differences.

The World Wars

You can understand and remember things more easily when you study their likenesses and differences. In this lesson, you will learn to compare and contrast as you read about two major events in world history.

---

1 KEYS to Comparing and Contrasting

Comparing and contrasting show likenesses and differences.

LEARN Comparing is used when referring to *likenesses* or *likenesses and differences*, while *contrasting* points out *differences*.

EXAMPLE Compare: Both wars involved many nations. Italy fought in both world wars but on different sides.
Contrast: Planes were significant in World War II, but not in the first war.

DIRECTIONS Read each sentence and write *compare* or *contrast* on the line.

1. World War I raged from 1914 to 1918, while World War II was fought from 1939 to 1945. _____

2. Both wars began in Europe, with World War I being triggered by two deadly shots aimed at one man, and Germany's invasion of Poland causing the onset of World War II._____

3. The United States, France, and England fought on the same side in both world wars. _____

⬤2 Practice Comparing and Contrasting

DIRECTIONS An *analogy* is often used to compare things or ideas:

1914 is to World War I as 1939 is to World War II.

The first two ideas have the same relationship as the last two, since 1914 was the start of World War I, and 1939 marked the beginning of World War II. An analogy is often written in a shorter way, using a colon in place of the words *is to,* and a double colon substituted for *as: 1914 : World War I :: 1939 : World War II.* Think about the relationship of the words on each side of the double colon and write the missing word to complete each analogy.

1. Two shots : World War I :: invasion : _____

2. _____ : World War II :: 1914 : World War I

3. Truce : World War I :: victory : _____

4. Argue : _____ :: agree : peace

5. World War I : W.W.I :: World War II : _____

DIRECTIONS An analogy may be written in different ways as long as the relationship of the two ideas on the left of the analogy is the same as the relationship of the ideas on the right.

Wartime is to grief as peacetime is to joy.
Wartime is to peacetime as grief is to joy.

In the first analogy, wartime is a time of grief, as peacetime is a time of joy. Similarly, wartime is the opposite of peacetime, as grief is the opposite of joy. Read each sentence and use the compared words to complete an analogy written two different ways.

1. The opponents in World War I were called the Allies and the Central Powers, while World War II saw the Allies fighting the Axis.

Allies is to _____ as Allies is to Axis

Allies is to _____ as Central Powers is to Axis

2. The United States fought along with the Allies to oppose Germany and the Central Powers in World War I.

_____ : Allies :: Germany : Central Powers

_____ : Central Powers :: United States : Germany

3 Read and Apply

DIRECTIONS Think about comparisons and contrasts as you read about the two world wars.

World War I began when two shots assassinated Archduke Ferdinand of Austria, but the desire of some countries to gain more and more power actually brought on the major conflict. The Allies, made up of Belgium, France, Great Britain, United States, Russia, Italy, Serbia, and many other countries, opposed Austria-Hungary, Bulgaria, Germany, and the Ottoman Empire as the Central Powers. Although a few vehicles, airplanes, and submarines were used, the war was primarily fought through hand-to-hand combat by soldiers from their trenches in Europe. The war raged for four years and finally ended in an armistice, or truce. Various peace treaties were signed and there was supposed to be world peace.

Many problems were unsolved, however. This fact, coupled with the rise to power by some dictators and the striving for more power by Ger-many, Italy, and Japan, led the world into a larger war twenty-one years later. Germany invaded Poland and World War II began. Germany, Italy, Japan, Hungary, and other nations joined forces as the Axis against the Allies, some fifty countries including Great Britain, France, Russia, United States, and Canada.

This time, the battlefields were not just in Europe. Fighting took place in Africa and in Southeast Asia. The weapons too, were different. No longer were the major battles fought solely from trenches. This was a war in the air and on the high seas. The atomic bomb was used for the first time when the United States bombed Hiroshima in Japan. The war continued for six years with the Allies claiming a decisive victory. There was again the hope of world peace, although there remained ill feelings among some nations.

The two world wars rank as the most costly wars in all modern history. Eight million people lost their lives in battle or from war-related causes during World War I, and another fifty-five million persons perished in World War II. In addition to the casualties, the wars cost money. World War I's cost of $337 billion was less than one third the cost of World War II, when expenditures mounted to $1,154 billion. In addition, property damage during the second war was estimated at $239 billion.

Both wars were devastating, but, fortunately, some lessons were learned. The Allies made an attempt to aid people who were left homeless and hungry in the war-torn countries after the first war. A greater effort was made after the second war when the Allies actively worked to assist Japan and Germany in rebuilding their war-ravaged countries.

DIRECTIONS Complete each pair of analogies to compare and contrast World Wars I and II.

1. Trench warfare : World War I :: atomic bomb : _____

   _____ : World War II :: trench warfare : atomic bomb

2. World War I : World War II :: _____ : $1,154 billion

   $1,154 billion : _____ :: $337 billion : World War I

3. 55 million deaths : _____ :: 8 million deaths : World War I

   World War I : World War II :: 8 million deaths : _____

DIRECTIONS Read the sentence and write your answer.

1. Compare the efforts of the Allies after World War I and World War II.

   _____

   _____

   _____

2. Contrast the world wars.

   _____

   _____

   _____

REMEMBER Compare and contrast for likenesses and differences.

Airships of the Future

You've probably seen pictures of a blimp or hot air balloon. Maybe you've even been lucky enough to see the real thing. In this lesson, you will learn about LTA's, lighter-than-air vehicles of the future. You will also learn how writers compare things to help you see a picture in your mind.

1 KEYS to Figurative Language

A simile is used to compare two things.

LEARN Authors often create a picture in your mind by comparing one thing to something else. We call the words they use *figures of speech*. One kind of figure of speech is a *simile* which uses the word *like* or *as*.

EXAMPLE *Kathy eats like a bird. This chili is as hot as fire.* The sentences are similes. Kathy and a bird are alike because they both eat very little. The chili's taste is compared to the heat of a fire.

DIRECTIONS Read the sentences and answer the questions.

1. The hot air balloon was as colorful as a patchwork quilt.
   What two things are being compared?

   1. _____ 2. _____

   How are they alike? _____

2. The blimp looked like a silver bullet floating above the football stadium.
   What two things are being compared?

   1. _____ 2. _____

   How are they alike? _____

2 Practice with Figurative Language

DIRECTIONS Underline the simile in each paragraph and tell what it means.

1. Mel felt like a deflated balloon. He had been so excited about flying all the way across the country to visit his old friend who'd moved to Denver. He was to leave in two days and now the trip plans were off. If only he could find a way to hide all these chicken pox! Would mom's make-up do the trick?

_____

_____

_____

2. Surely her mom would agree. All she had to do was convince her. After all, she and Paula were like sisters. They simply couldn't be apart for two whole weeks! Mom would surely see that she just had to get signed up for the same camp as Paula.

_____

_____

3. "Oh, no!" sighed Angela as she searched frantically through her backpack. "It has to be here! I remember packing it with my books! She rummaged some more. Then she felt a prick like the point of a needle. "There is is! Thank goodness! I found my compass."

_____

_____

_____

4. The search was on, though they knew their chances of finding it were as good as winning the lottery. The contact lens had to be somewhere in the room, since Uncle Bob had not moved from the dining room all day.

_____

_____

_____

5. The curtains closed on the first scene and everything seemed to be going well. The audience's laughter and applause were more than the players had ever hoped for. Yet Paul stood deep in thought. What if he had a sudden itch that had to be scratched when he was supposed to stand as still as a mannequin?

_____

_____

DIRECTIONS Look for similes as you read about airships of the future. Then underline each simile.

Look! Up in the sky! It's a bird! It's a plane! No . . . it's a house! Yes, someday you just may see houses being lifted through the sky as if they were as weightless as feathers! You may see other heavy cargo such as tons of lumber being transported through the air like toothpicks. What you now recognize as hot-air balloons or blimps may be like trucks in the air in the future. These lighter-than-air ships, or LTA's, are as big as skyscrapers and may be the cruisers and haulers of the future.

LTA's were called "limps" by the British during World War I. Since the most common design was the type B limp, they soon were called blimps. Although earlier blimps were filled with hydrogen, LTA's are now lifted like balloons by helium.

Blimps have long been used like small planes to carry sightseers or photographers. Inventors predict, however, that the new LTA's will do more than carry people. They will be able to transport loads of up to eighty tons and travel thousands of miles without touching down. Unlike jetliners, an LTA in flight is as quiet as a sleeping baby. No longer do all LTA's look like fat cigars. Several new designs are in the works, from a spheric shape like a baseball to a tall and narrow model that looks something like an eggbeater.

Strange as they may look, the new LTA's just may be the solution for lifting and moving heavy loads like gigantic trees from a forest or a derailed train. Using their ability to hover like a helicopter, LTA's may even be used for firefighting in forests or to clean up after an oil freighter has lost its cargo in the ocean.

DIRECTIONS Circle the words that best complete each sentence.

1. LTA's are *like a giant bubble* means
   a. they move through the air.
   b. you can see through them.
   c. they are made of soap and water.

2. LTA's may look *like baseballs* means
   a. the same size as baseballs.
   b. white with red stitching.
   c. round.

3. If blimps look *like fat cigars,*
   a. they are brown.
   b. they have a long oval shape.
   c. they have smoke coming out of them.

4. LTA's might work *like cranes* means
   a. they could put out a forest fire.
   b. they could lift something heavy.
   c. people would not need to build new roads.

5. An LTA is *like a helicopter* means
   a. it can stay in the air in one spot.
   b. it can clean oil spills.
   c. it can lift a train that has gone off the track.

DIRECTIONS Write one of the four similes to complete each sentence.

as tall as a mountain   like eyes in the sky
as light as a feather   as quiet as a whisper

1. A heavy load might be _____ for an LTA.

2. When blimps carry people in the air to see or photograph things, they are

_____ .

3. An LTA in flight is _____ .

4. A blimp's size may be _____ .

REMEMBER A simile uses the words *like* or *as* to compare things.

Idioms and Cliches

Are you happy as a lark today? If you try to catch someone's eye, are you waiting to catch an eyeball? In this lesson, you'll learn about these and other figures of speech as you read about a fellow who successfully solved a problem.

KEYS to Figurative Language

Idioms and cliches are two kinds of figurative language.

LEARN   An *idiom* is a figure of speech used to give the reader a sharp picture in the mind. The *literal*, or actual, meaning of an idiom is different from its *figurative* meaning. If you took it literally, you might want a glove to help catch the eyeball. Figuratively, the expression means *to get someone's attention*. We use context (the words around a figure of speech) to help us grasp the meaning.

DIRECTIONS   Circle the idiom in each sentence. Then write *L* for literal or *F* for figurative before each meaning.

1. Alison was frustrated and told her brother to get lost.

   _____ go away where no one can find you

   _____ stop bothering me

2. I was all bottled up inside when I heard the news.

   _____ upset or frustrated

   _____ put in a bottle

3. My friend and I are two peas in a pod.

   _____ very much alike

   _____ green vegetables in a shell

4. My dad is forever pulling my leg.

   _____ tugging on my leg

   _____ teasing me

Practice With Figurative Language

DIRECTIONS Some figures of speech, called clichés (pronounced kle-SHAS), have been used so often they lose their effectiveness. You could express extreme hunger by using the cliché *hungry as a bear* or say a person works *like a horse* to describe a hardworking nature. Underline each cliché in the story. Then circle the best meaning for each.

"Chuck, you have a heart of gold," said Richie, who was grateful to have help with his homework. "I know you helped me because we are true blue friends."

"I'll be your friend till the bitter end," said Chuck, "but as a word to the wise, don't wait until the last minute to do your homework."

"I should know better. The last time I was late, I thought my teacher would kill me," Richie said. "I'm going to turn over a new leaf. Just wait and see!"

1. *A heart of gold* means
   very busy.   very kind.
   angry.   impatient.

2. *True blue* means
   loyal.   old.
   honest.   lazy.

3. *Till the bitter end* means
   always.   today.
   funny.   soon.

4. *A word to the wise* means
   warning.   joke.
   ignore.   critical.

5. *Would kill me* means
   praise.   replace.
   hug.   reprimand.

6. *Turn over a new leaf* means
   change.   plan.
   wonderful.   lie.

Read and Apply

DIRECTIONS Think about idioms as you read about how Chad solved a real problem.

Chad was *about to explode.* He had taken all the teasing he could tolerate and after some careful planning, he decided to quit being the *fall guy.* He would *give them some of their own medicine.*

Ever since the first grading period, the guys had been *on Chad's back* for making good grades. They said he was a "goody goody" for always turning in his assignments on time and being "Johnny on the spot" when Mr. Hershel asked for volunteers. The guys were really being *two-faced,* since they never hesitated to run to him for help on their own work. Well, he'd fix them! He'd stop helping them study the way he'd done all year. Yes, he'd just let them *sink or swim* on their own. Maybe then they'd stop.

He put his plan into action. Later that day when Mel came over with some fraction problems he didn't understand, Chad said he had to run to soccer practice. That night, when Geoff called with an English assignment that he claimed was impossible, Chad begged off, saying he had to feed his pets before his mom got home. The next day at school, Chad was conveniently busy when two of the guys had questions on their science project.

Several days later, Chad noticed the teasing had ceased. Instead, the guys seemed to be seeking him out and not just for help with their work, either. They wanted him on their team in gym class and he was never alone as he rode home on his bike.

Chad was proud of the way he had solved his problem. He'd ended the teasing and gained friends in the process.

DIRECTIONS Write the idioms from the story and the figurative and literal meaning for each.

1. Idiom: _____

_____

Figurative Meaning: _____

_____

_____

Literal Meaning: _____

_____

_____

2. Idiom: _____

_____

Figurative Meaning: _____

_____

_____

Literal Meaning: _____

_____

_____

3. Idiom: _____

_____

Figurative Meaning: _____

_____

_____

Literal Meaning: _____

_____

_____

4. Idiom: _____

_____

Figurative Meaning: _____

_____

_____

Literal Meaning: _____

_____

_____

5. Idiom: _____

_____

Figurative Meaning: _____

_____

_____

Literal Meaning: _____

_____

_____

6. Idiom: _____

_____

Figurative Meaning: _____

_____

_____

Literal Meaning: _____

_____

_____

REMEMBER Use context to get the meaning of an idiom or cliché.

Remembering Not To Forget

An old gimmick suggests tying a string around your finger to help you remember something. In this lesson, you'll learn some memory tips that are even more helpful.

 ## KEYS to Memory

Memory tips or *mnemonic devices* can jog your memory.

LEARN A sentence, phrase, rhyme, idea, or comparison can help us remember something difficult. *Mnemonic devices* are helpful in remembering lists of things, the meaning or spelling of a word, or other things you want to remember.

EXAMPLE *Every good boy does fine* is a mnemonic device which helps us remember that the names and order of the music notes on the lines of the treble clef are *E, G, B, D,* and *F.* The word *face* reminds us that the notes in the spaces are *F, A, C,* and *E.*

DIRECTIONS Circle the letter of the best answer.

1. Which idea might help you remember how to spell the word *vacuum?*

    a. The word has two syllables.

    b. The extra *u* helps suck up more dirt.

    c. The word begins with *v.*

    d. The *c* comes after the *a.*

2. Which idea could be helpful in remembering the difference in the spelling of the words *desert* and *dessert?*

    a. *Dessert* has two *s's* like summer *s*howers.

    b. A *desert* is dry, so it has only one *s.*

    c. *Dessert* has more *s's* because you always want more dessert.

    d. All of the above

Practice Using Memory Tricks

DIRECTIONS Read each paragraph and complete the sentences.

1. "That's it! That's how I can remember that stalagmites come up from the floor of a cave and stalactites hang down from the ceiling!" said Willie as he gazed at the photos in the encyclopedia. "The stalactites have to hold *tight* to keep from falling!"

   a. The mineral deposits jutting up from the floor of a cave are called _____ .

   b. The deposits suspended from the ceiling of a cave are called

   _____ .

2. Mnemonic devices are often written in rhyme. This poem helps to remember when to spell a word with *ie* or with *ei*.

   I before *e*
   Except after *c*,
   Or when sounded like *a*
   As in *neighbor* or *weigh*.
   But what about *seizure*,
   And *weird*—also *leisure*,
   Fahrenheit, *neither*,
   Forfeit, *height*, *either*?

   a. She had worked hard and now was taking some

   _____ time.

   b. It was 82° _____ according to the thermometer.

   c. Did you _____ the package I mailed to your house?

   d. If something is extremely odd or unusual, we say it is

   _____ .

   e. I hope we can be

   _____ instead of enemies.

3. Synonyms are words that mean the same or nearly the same, while antonyms are words that mean the opposite. A good way to prevent confusing the two words is to remember that *s* begins both *synonym* and *same*.

   a. The words *delighted* and *overjoyed* are examples of

   _____ .

   b. *Brief* and *lengthy* are examples of _____ .

   c. A _____ for *splendid* is *marvelous*.

   d. *Grief* and *joy* have opposite meanings and are

   _____ .

Read and Apply

DIRECTIONS Read about a mnemonic device that saved the day.

"Washington, Adams, Jefferson, Madison, uh, Monroe, Jackson, no, no, no! Washington, Adams, Jefferson, Madison, Monroe, *Adams*, Jackson, Harrison, no, *Van Buren*, Harrison . . . I can't do this!" exclaimed Alison in a frustrated voice.

"What can't you do?" called her grandmother from the kitchen.

"I'll never get all the presidents in the right order, and I have to say them perfectly tomorrow in social studies class!" wailed Alison.

"Here's one time when I can help you with your homework!" said her grandmother, proudly. "Do you know the president's names pretty well, Alison?"

"Yes, I know their names fairly well, but I just can't say them in order," replied her granddaughter.

"You will soon. When I was young, my teacher told us that to remember the presidents in order, all we had to do was learn a sentence. Each word in the sentence begins with the same first letter as a president's last name. I've

always remembered that sentence. Every time a new president was elected, I changed the sentence just a little."

"That must be a *long* sentence, Grandma! There have been forty presidents."

"It's long, all right, but once you learn it, you'll never forget it *or* the order of the presidents. Here's how it goes: When a joke made me a joker, Van had to poke the fiery poker, but long John Grant had good, acute, clear hearing, catching many rat tails with heavy cow halter rope, that even Katie Johnson's nimble fingers couldn't rescue."

Alison wrote the sentence exactly as her grandmother dictated it. Then she underlined the first letter of each word in the sentence. She looked at those first letters as she rapidly named the presidents, "Washington, Adams, Jefferson, Madison, Monroe, Adams, Jackson, Van Buren, Harrison, Tyler, Polk, Taylor, Fillmore, Pierce, Buchanan, Lincoln, Johnson, Grant, Hayes, Garfield, Arthur, Cleveland, Harrison, Cleveland, McKinley, Roosevelt, Taft, Wilson, Harding, Coolidge, Hoover, Roosevelt, Truman, Eisenhower, Kennedy, Johnson, Nixon, Ford, Carter, Reagan! Whew! I did it, Grandma! Thanks! All my classmates will want to copy this. It makes this job a cinch! Uh, Grandma, you wouldn't happen to have a tip on the states and their capitals, too, would you?"

Write Alison's mnemonic device, one word beside each number. Circle the first letter of each word. Then write the correct president's name beside each word.

	Word	President		Word	President
1.			21.		
2.			22.		
3.			23.		
4.			24.		
5.			25.		
6.			26.		
7.			27.		
8.			28.		
9.			29.		
10.			30.		
11.			31.		
12.			32.		
13.			33.		
14.			34.		
15.			35.		
16.			36.		
17.			37.		
18.			38.		
19.			39.		
20.			40.		

REMEMBER Learn or make up your own mnemonic device to remember things.

A Picture Is Worth A Thousand Words

In this lesson, you'll learn about the clues you can find in pictures.

KEYS to Picture Interpretation

Pictures can help you understand ideas.

LEARN Pictures help fill your mind with ideas to better understand an author's message. A caption under a picture can summarize a main idea in the picture.

DIRECTIONS Study the picture and complete the idea sentences.

1. This campsite may be located in _____.

2. The campers traveled to this campsite by _____.

3. The reason these people are camping here is that _____
_____.

4. A good caption for this picture might be _____
_____.

② Practice Picture Interpretation

DIRECTIONS Study the savage drama taking place in the painting of the Old West. The artist has captured the action of a bison hunt. Think about the story the painting shares. Use the facts you gather to answer the questions.

1. What weapons did the Crow Indians use in the bison hunt?

_____

_____

2. Which picture clues tell you that the bison hunt was a dangerous activity at times?

_____

_____

3. Why did the Crow men isolate the bison into small groups?

_____

_____

4. What sounds would you expect to hear if you could go back in time and be a witness to this hunt?

_____

_____

5. Why do you think bison hunts such as the one shown here were necessary?

_____

_____

Read and Apply

DIRECTIONS Read about some purposes for pictures.

"I use pictures in my books because sometimes words just can't express my ideas well enough," said Ms. Sandaker. "Take this picture for instance. Since this book is about exploring in the Arctic, I wanted the reader to feel the frosty feeling of sub-zero temperatures and the hardship. I felt that all the cold words in our language would not give you that feeling as well as this one picture could."

"I felt that this picture would make the written ideas more interesting. This book," she went on, "is harder to read, so I used pictures like this to make the difficult ideas easier to understand."

"I read that book," interjected Simon, "or most of it, anyway. I especially like the pictures."

"If you liked that book, I'll bet you read this one easily," continued the author. "When I compiled this book, I wanted my readers to add some of their own ideas about what this fellow must have been like. There's very little known about him, yet there are many pictures of him in the archives. He must have been a real character, judging from his pictures."

Simon hadn't read this new book, but the fellow in the pictures immediately caught his attention. He began to leaf through the book as Ms. Sandaker paused to autograph another customer's purchase. One particular picture caused Simon to chuckle.

"Well, I see I was successful!" Ms. Sandaker remarked as she returned the autographed book. "I put that picture in there to add a bit of humor. Sometimes, I think, a picture is worth a thousand words and your chuckle proves it!"

List 5 reasons an author might use pictures.

a. _____

b. _____

c. _____

d. _____

e. _____

DIRECTIONS Study each numbered picture, and read its caption. Then answer the questions by writing the number of a picture on the line.

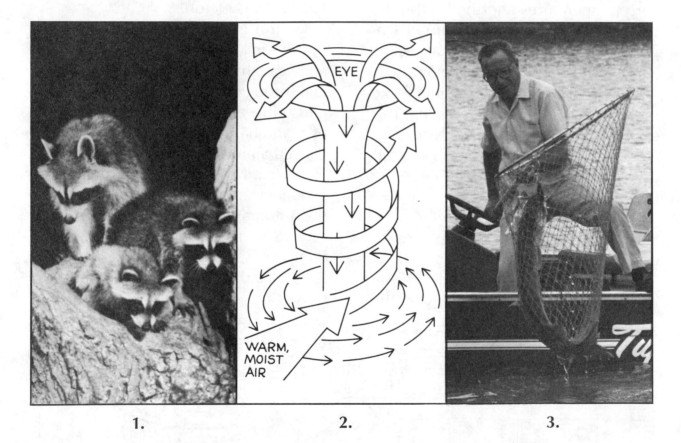

1.   2.   3.

_____ **1.** Which picture might help you understand a hurricane?

_____ **2.** Which picture might help you appreciate the author's love of wildlife in a national forest?

_____ **3.** Which picture might give you more ideas about somebody's interests and hobbies?

REMEMBER A picture can give you many clues.

Facts About Places

People have drawn special pictures of the earth since long ago. In this lesson, you'll learn about maps, or graphic presentations, of places on earth.

1 KEYS to Maps

Maps show places or information about places.

LEARN *General reference maps* show particular places on the earth's surface. Transportation or road maps are general reference maps, as are globes and the charts used by pilots of planes. *Physical* and *political* maps are types of *thematic maps*. Physical maps show mountains, or sea level, while political maps show boundaries or population. Other thematic maps show rainfall, industries, or languages.

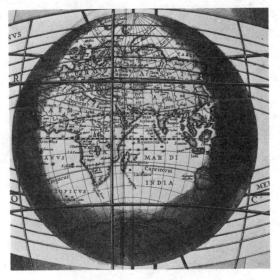

DIRECTIONS Write *general reference* or *thematic* on the line to tell the type of map described in each sentence.

1. We used a globe to find the seven continents. _____

2. We used a map of waterways to find the river. _____

3. Our city's map shows all the newest streets. _____

4. Maurie and Cal used a map that showed the kinds of industry found in each state of the United States. _____

Practice With Maps

DIRECTIONS Cartographers, or map makers, use *symbols* and *colors* to show things on maps. A *legend* explains each symbol or color. Distances on maps are shown by use of a *scale* where one inch or centimeter represents a particular distance. Study each map and answer the questions below it.

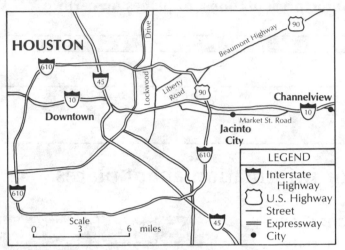

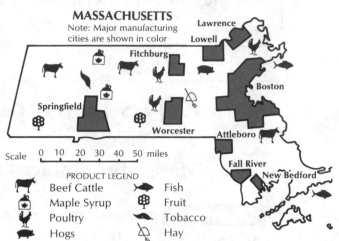

1. Is this a general reference or thematic map?

   _____

2. What Interstate circles the city of Houston?

   _____

3. If one inch represents 6 miles, how far is the city of Channelview from Jacinto City?

   _____

4. What highway would you travel to go from Channelview to downtown Houston?

   _____

5. What other name is given to Beaumont Highway?

   _____

1. Is this map a general reference or thematic map?

   _____

2. How many areas rely heavily on the fishing industry?

   _____

3. Name the two largest manufacturing cities in Massachusetts.

   _____

   _____

4. What industries are found near Worcester?

   _____

5. How many areas rely on the beef cattle industry?

   _____

DIRECTIONS Read this sketch of the history of maps.

Imagine coming home to tell about your travels to a place never before explored by anyone. You're so excited about the new land you've seen that you attempt to draw a map to add to your description. Such were the travel experiences of the first map makers. They had no idea of the vastness of the earth, for their travels were limited, as were their maps.

Although maps may have been made even earlier, the oldest known map dates to 2300 B.C. This clay tablet map is evidence that people scratched out graphic representations of the land on any material available.

The ancient Greeks and Romans made maps in the third century B.C., although only a few of the Roman maps are available today. Around 150 B.C., a scholar named Ptolemy made many maps from which the first atlas was eventually developed some twelve-hundred years later. One map made by a well-known cartographer, Christopher Columbus, exists today as evidence that he, like other travelers after his time, mapped the places he explored.

The combined use of several inventions in the early 1900's contributed to the art of map making. The invention of the automobile brought about the need for transportation maps. Maps continued to be made from the knowledge of land-travelers, until it was discovered that cameras could take pictures of the land from high above in airplanes. Maps could be made from these photos. The introduction of computers and radar devices have also changed the world of cartography.

What a long way we've come from the days of scratching out a graphic description of an area on the other side of town!

There can be as many different special or thematic maps as there are special things to show. Study the thematic maps. Then complete the sentences below.

1. More than _____ people live in each square mile in Portland, Maine.

2. There are _____ centimeters of precipitation per year in Monterrey, Mexico.

3. Caribou, Maine has _____ to _____people living in each square mile.

4. Acapulco has _____ inches of moisture per year.

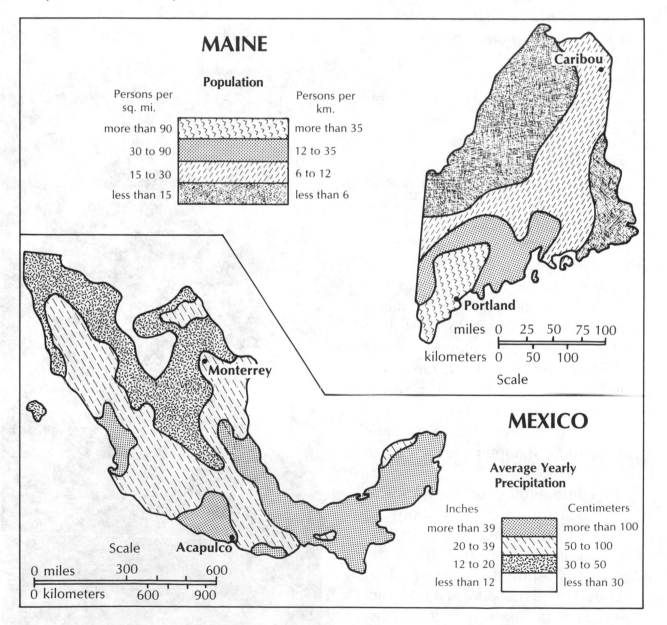

MAINE

Population

Persons per sq. mi.		Persons per km.
more than 90		more than 35
30 to 90		12 to 35
15 to 30		6 to 12
less than 15		less than 6

Caribou

Portland

miles 0 25 50 75 100

kilometers 0 50 100

Scale

MEXICO

Monterrey

Acapulco

Average Yearly Precipitation

Inches		Centimeters
more than 39		more than 100
20 to 39		50 to 100
12 to 20		30 to 50
less than 12		less than 30

Scale

0 miles 300 600

0 kilometers 600 900

REMEMBER Different kinds of maps tell different things.

Graphing Facts

Sometimes it helps to *see* a group of facts rather than just read a paragraph containing facts. In this lesson you will learn about four different kinds of graphs.

1 KEYS to Graphs

Graphs show how facts compare to one another.

LEARN Graphs let you see information quickly. A graph's *title* tells you the kind of information being shown. A *key* may explain abbreviations or symbols. In a *picture graph,* one picture may represent a larger number of objects, while a partial picture represents part of a large number.

EXAMPLE

Key = 100 bicycles

BIKES SOLD IN 1986	
CITY	NUMBER
Detroit	🚲 🚲 🚲 🚲 🚲
Houston	🚲 🚲 🚲 🚲 🚲 🚲 🚲 🚲
Kalamazoo	🚲 🚲 🚲 🚲 🚲

The picture graph tells that there were 750 bikes sold in Houston.

DIRECTIONS Use facts in the above graph to answer the questions.

1. One-half bicycle represents how many bicycles? _____

2. What calendar year is summarized by this graph? _____

3. In which city did customers purchase the most bicycles? _____

4. Which city sold more bicycles, Detroit or Kalamazoo? _____

Graphs **153**

② Practice With Graphs

DIRECTIONS A *pie graph*, sometimes called a *circle graph*, is used to compare parts to a whole. Each labeled piece, or wedge, of a pie graph represents a part of the whole. Read about Timothy's plan to earn $180.00 for a new bicycle. Then use facts from the pie graph to answer the questions below.

When Timothy wanted to buy a new ten-speed bicycle, the best buy he found was at Matt's Cycle shop. He considered the price of $180.00 and began to plan how he would save over the next six months to make the purchase. Timothy planned seven different sources of income to collect the money he'd need, and then he drew a graph to show his total plan.

MY BICYCLE BUDGET

1. How much of Timothy's money will come from holiday gifts?

   _____

2. What seems to be Timothy's best source of income?

   _____

3. How does Tim plan to earn the $40 listed in his plan?

   _____

4. Is babysitting or lawn work more profitable for Tim?

   _____

5. Which two sources of his money are expected to be equal?

   _____ and

   _____

6. Which source of income is least profitable?

   _____

7. What is the total amount of money shown on Tim's graph?

   _____

8. How much money does Timothy plan to use from his savings?

Read and Apply

DIRECTIONS A *bar graph,* using bar-like shapes placed closely together, allows you to compare facts easily. Labels are located on each *axis,* or *side,* of a bar graph. The bottom of a bar graph is called the *horizontal axis,* while the side is the *vertical axis.* Each axis gives information.

A bar graph may be shown with vertical or horizontal bars. The vertical axis on the "Books Read" bar graph below tells the number of books read by some students in Mr. Jacob's class during the first semester. The horizontal axis tells the names of the students. The students' names are listed on the vertical axis of the "Authors Read" bar graph which shows the number of different authors represented in each student's reading. Study the bar graphs and answer the questions below.

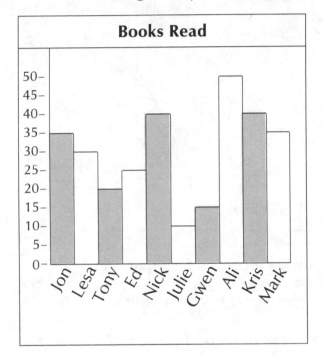

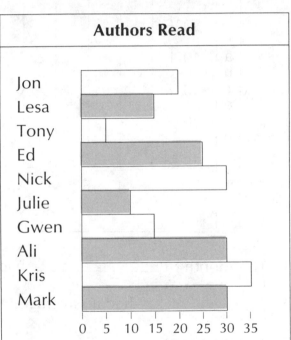

1. How many books did Nick read?

_____

2. Did Lesa or Nick read more books?

_____

3. How do you know that Tony read several books by the same author?

_____

4. Which student read the most books?

_____

5. Who read the least number of books?

_____

6. Who read books representing the most different authors?

_____

DIRECTIONS A *line graph* can be used to show changes over a period of time. A line graph has a *grid,* or set of parallel bars. Facts are recorded on the bars. The horizontal axis and vertical axis show facts much like those on a bar graph. Study the line graph. Then answer the questions.

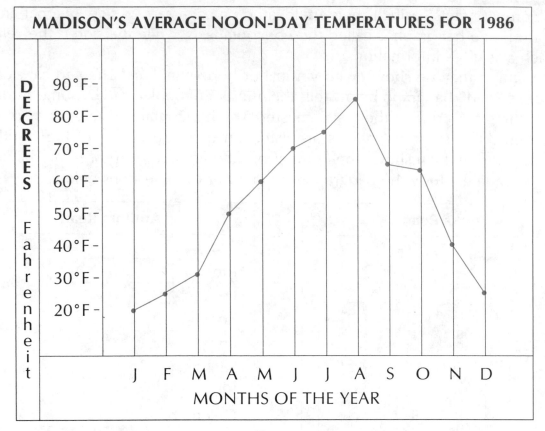

1. The month of _____ had the lowest recorded temperature.

2. _____ had an average temperature equal to December's.

3. The month of _____ shows the peak or highest point on the line graph.

4. Write the four months with the lowest temperatures.

_____   _____   _____   _____

5. The average temperature in _____ was 30° less than that of October.

6. The horizontal axis shows _____.

7. The vertical axis shows _____.

REMEMBER Graphs are visual aids for gaining facts quickly.

Tables Without Legs

What kind of table has no legs? In this lesson, you'll learn about some tables that have no legs but instead contain facts.

1 KEYS to Tables

A table is an organized list of facts.

LEARN   A table organizes facts so they're easy to find. The *title* tells the topic. Facts are listed in *rows* and *columns*. A *heading* begins each row or column. Read *across a row* and *down a column* to find a fact. The last row or column of a number table may give totals.

EXAMPLE   To find the number of cans Lee collected the third week, go across the *Week 3 row* to the *Lee column*. Lee collected 198 cans.

Aluminum Can Collections

	Heidi	Jenna	Lee	Lesa	Paul	Tim	Total
Week 1	120	201	110	246	214	298	1,189
Week 2	180	70	146	162	169	116	843
Week 3	136	148	198	119	278	225	1,104
Week 4	100	116	186	228	118	247	995
Total	536	535	640	755	779	886	4,131

DIRECTIONS Use the above table to complete the statements.

1. _____ collected the most cans during the third week.

2. Jenna collected more cans than _____ during the fourth week.

3. The six students collected a total of _____ cans.

4. _____ was the top collector for weeks 1 and 4 and for the entire project.

② Practice With Tables

DIRECTIONS Read about Matthew's collection of facts. Then use his table to answer the questions.

Matthew asked some of his classmates to participate in a survey. The purpose of his survey was to find out what kinds of sports equipment were used most often. Matthew used the *symbol X* to record facts as he orga-nized them to make a table. Each row in his table tells about a different person's equipment. Each column tells about a particular type of sports equipment.

Most Popular Sports Equipment

	10-speed	Dirt Bike	Skateboard	Ice Skates	Roller Skates	Skis
Emily	X				X	
Jay	X	X		X		X
Chris	X	X		X	X	
Matthew	X	X	X	X	X	X
Lindsey			X		X	X
Donna			X		X	
Daniel	X				X	X

1. How many classmates said they used roller skates often?

_____

2. Which classmate claimed to use all the items on the list?

_____

3. What kind of bike does Emily ride?

_____

4. What's the total number of bikes on Matthew's table?

_____

5. Do Matthew's friends use skate-boards or roller skates more?

_____

6. If Chris went ice skating, which friends might be there?

_____

7. Which kind of sporting equipment is the most popular?

_____

8. Which classmates enjoy four or more different sports?

_____

9. How many students enjoy some form of skating?

_____

Read and Apply

Read about a well-made table that caused some extra work.

When Miss Olson's class studied some countries and their governments, Maurice and David decided to do a cooperative project for extra credit. After some discussion, the boys decided they'd each take five countries which interested them and study the life of each country's leader or head of state. They'd compile the information they gained and make an oral report in two weeks.

A few days later, David and Maurice discussed what they'd learned so far and found they'd chosen too big a topic. They would never be able to include all the information they were finding on some of the heads of state, and for others they found no information other than about the official's home.

It was then that the boys changed their plans. Since they were both interested in the official homes they'd been learning about, it seemed they should limit their report to the homes of some heads of state. They decided to make a table to use as a visual aid for their oral report.

Maurice took the countries of Australia, West Germany, Spain, Mexico, and the United Kingdom, while David was responsible for Italy, Belgium, United States, France, and Portugal. Each boy contributed to the making of the table with David writing that the king of Belgium resides in the Chateau de Lachen in Brussels, and the home of the president of France is at L'Elysee Palace in Paris. Maurice filled in some information about the United Kingdom's prime minister living at Number 10 Downing Street in London, England.

The boys found that Miss Olson especially liked their table, perhaps too much! She announced that the next test would include the information on their table.

Use information from the story you just read to fill in the missing facts in the table. Then use the table to circle the best answer for each question below.

Homes for Heads of Government

Country	Name of Home	Leader's Title	Location
Australia	The Lodge	Prime Minister	Canberra
Belgium	_____	_____	_____
France	_____	_____	_____
Italy	Quiranale	President	Rome
Mexico	Los Pinos	President	Mexico City
Portugal	Palacio de Belem	President	Lisbon
Spain	Palacio de la Moncloe	Premier	Madrid
West Germany	Federal Chancellor's Office	Chancellor	Bonn
United Kingdom	_____		_____
United States	The White House	President	Washington, D.C.

1. If you visited Canberra, Australia, which official government home could you see?

   The White House   The Lodge

   Chateau de Lachen   Los Pinos

2. Where is the Chateau de Lachen located?

   France   Spain

   Germany   Belgium

3. What is the title of the head of government in Paris, France?

   Premier   President

   Chancellor   King

4. In what city does the President of Mexico live?

   Rome   London

   Mexico City   Canberra

5. Which country is not ruled by a president?

   Italy   Australia

   Portugal   Mexico

6. Which country's leader lives in Palacio de la Moncloe?

   Spain   Australia

   Portugal   Belgium

7. Which government is headed by a King?

   France   Belgium

   Australia   United States

8. Which is the only country listed that is led by a chancellor?

   West Germany   Portugal

   Italy   France

REMEMBER Tables can have numbers, words, or symbols.

Picture This

Sometimes an idea is easier if you have a drawing to help you picture it. In this lesson, you'll learn about special pictures that explain some ideas about spider webs and other things.

 KEYS to Diagrams

A diagram is a detailed picture that explains an idea.

LEARN Some diagrams explain objects by showing all their parts. Other diagrams help you understand an idea by showing a step-by-step process. A diagram may be labeled with words, numbers, or symbols.

EXAMPLE

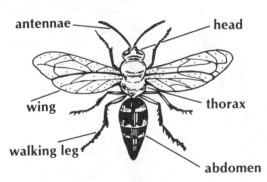

antennae — head

wing

walking leg

thorax

abdomen

An insect has _____ walking legs.
(number)

These legs are all attached to the

_____ . The _____
(number)

antennae are attached to the

_____ of the insect. The abdomen of an insect is attached to the

_____ .

DIRECTIONS Consult the diagram. Then read the question at the right and circle the number of the best definition.

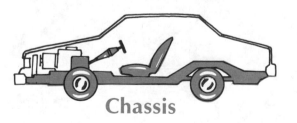

Chassis

Which meaning does the diagram illustrate?

chassis (chas'e) **n.** **1** the framework of an automobile, including all parts except the engine and body. **2** the framework that holds the working parts of a radio or television set.

② Practice With Diagrams

DIRECTIONS Study the diagram and the chart. Use the facts as you answer the questions.

STEER

Steer Part	*Meat Cut*
1. Chuck	Chuck roast, ground chuck
2. Rib	Prime rib, short ribs
3. Short Loin	Porterhouse and T-bone steaks
4. Sirloin	Sirloin roast and steak
5. Round	Rump roast, round roast, ground round
6. Flank	Flank steak, hamburger
7. Short Plate	Braised beef, hamburger

1. Meat cuts taken from the upper middle portion of a steer are the most tender, costly pieces. Which would be the most costly steak, a flank or a T-bone?

_____

2. Does sirloin roast come from the front or back quarter of beef?

_____

3. From which two parts of a steer do we get hamburger?

_____

_____

4. Do short ribs of beef come from the front half or the hind half of a steer?

_____

5. What meat cuts do you get from the steer part labeled number 5 on the diagram

_____

_____

Read and Apply

DIRECTIONS A series of diagrams can help explain a step-by-step process. Captions below each part of a diagram help explain the ideas. Read about orb-weaving spiders. Study the diagrams and read the captions.

Orb-weaving spiders are spectacular architects. These spiders use their silk to weave intricate webs that are built during the night and actually eaten by the spider early the next morning. Below is a series of diagrams which show the steps that orb-weaving spiders go through as they construct their webs.

HOW THE WEB OF AN ORB-WEAVING SPIDER IS MADE

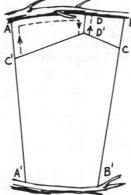
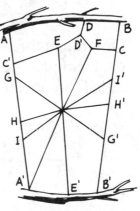

1. The spider begins by dropping thread from A on top branch to A' on bottom branch. Then it climbs back up that thread, along the branch to B, and drops down to B'. It returns and starts a new thread at C. It trails this thread as it climbs on up and across the branch and down thread A-A' to C'.

2. The spider climbs back up to the branch and drops a new thread at D. This is secured around thread C-C' and pulled tight.

3. From the thread C-C', the spider drops to the lower branch for the first radial thread, then weaves the other radial lines.

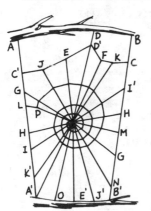
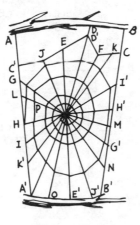
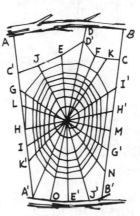
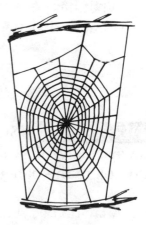

4. After completing the radial thread system, the spider begins the primary spiral. Neither of these is sticky.

5. The sticky threads follow, working from the outside and in toward the center of the web.

6. As the spider nears the center of the web, it cuts away the primary spiral, replacing it with the viscid thread.

7. In the finished web, the primary thread has been removed, leaving the heavy supporting framework and the spiral of sticky thread.

Use information from the diagrams and their captions on the previous page to complete the sentences.

1. Does an orb-weaving spider ever climb along the silk threads of its web during the construction?

   _____

2. What is the number of the diagram that shows the spider's first radial thread?

   _____

3. One radial thread goes from G to G'. Name all the other paths of the radial threads:

   _____to_____   _____ to _____

   _____to_____   _____to_____

4. What does an orb-weaving spider begin to work on once the radial threads have been spun?

   _____

5. What happens to the primary spiral during step 6 of the diagram?

   _____

   _____

DIRECTIONS Study the diagram of lawn volleyball. Use the facts as you complete the paragraphs.

   A lawn volleyball court is divided into two equal parts with each side of the court _____ feet long and _____ feet wide. The total length of the volleyball court is

_____ feet. The court is divided down the middle by the

_____. At each end of the court is a serving area.

Each of these areas is _____ feet wide.

   At the beginning of a volleyball game, there are at least _____ players on the court. The player positioned directly in front of each serving area is called the

_____. Each team has a _____ in the middle of the front row. The symbol used to represent players on the top half of the court is a _____. The symbol that represents players on the bottom half is a _____.

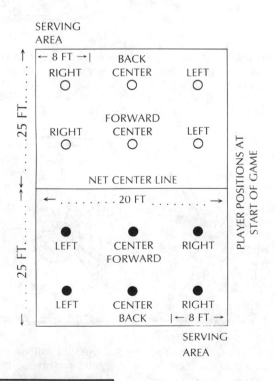

REMEMBER A diagram is a drawing of an idea.

The Secret Mission

Your schedule for today is probably in your head or, perhaps, in a special planbook. Schedules are important to help us be at the right place at the right time. In this lesson, you'll learn to read different kinds of schedules. You'll also read about a secret mission.

KEYS to Reading Schedules

A schedule tells times and dates of events.

LEARN A schedule is a special kind of table whose title tells its topic. Key words or numbers in a schedule help you quickly locate the specific information you want.

EXAMPLE If you wanted to ride a bus to North Pinckney Street on Wednesday morning, you'd look under *East Mifflin and North Pinckney* on the *AM* section of the schedule.

DIRECTIONS Consult the bus schedule to complete each statement.

1. If I want to be at Sherman Plaza before 5:30 P.M., I can

   take the _____ , _____ , or _____ bus.

2. The only days I cannot get to Commanche by bus are

   _____ and _____ .

3. I will need to get _____ for a dollar to buy
   my one ticket.

SHERMAN EXPRESS
EXACT FARE REQUIRED

ADULTS	5¢ WITH
40¢	**$13** MONTHLY PASS

No Charge for Transfers

CHILDREN	STUDENTS
Under 5 Years	**30¢**
ACCOMPANIED	in high
WITH AN	school
ADULT	or under
FREE	18 years

WEEKDAYS ONLY
AM

Wheeler & Commanche	Sherman Plaza	E. Mifflin & N. Pinckney	Univ. & Breese Ter.
6:25	6:40	6:55	7:05
6:45	7:00	7:15	7:25G
7:05	7:20	7:35	7:45G
7:25	7:40	7:55	8:05G

PM

Univ. & Breese Ter.	State St. & W. Mifflin	Sherman Plaza	Wheeler & Commanche
3:55	4:10	4:25	4:35
4:15	4:30	4:45	4:55G
4:35	4:50	5:05	5:15G
4:55	5:15	5:30	5:40G

DIRECTIONS Study the work schedule Myrt posted for his fast-food restaurant employees. Answer the questions.

WORK SCHEDULE FOR May 31–June 4
Dates and Times

	May 31	June 1	June 2	June 3	June 4
Gerry	8:00 A.M. 4:00 P.M.			2:00 P.M. 10:00 P.M.	
Sandy		8:00 A.M. 4:00 P.M.	8:00 A.M. 4:00 P.M.		4:00 P.M. 11:00 P.M.
Vern	2:00 P.M. 10:00 P.M.			8:00 A.M. 4:00 P.M.	4:00 P.M. 11:00 P.M.
Bonnie		2:00 P.M. 10:00 P.M.	2:00 P.M. 10:00 P.M.		
Dee	2:00 P.M. 10:00 P.M.		2:00 P.M. 10:00 P.M.		8:00 A.M. 4:00 P.M.
Willy		2:00 P.M. 10:00 P.M.		8:00 A.M. 4:00 P.M.	

1. Who will report to work at Myrt's at 8:00 A.M. on June 2?

_____

2. Would Bonnie be free to play softball at 9:00 P.M. on June 2?

_____

3. What time does Dee finish working on June 2?

_____

4. Which two workers begin work at 2:00 P.M. on June 2?

_____ _____

5. On which date is Myrt's open the latest?

_____

6. Who is the first employee to arrive at Myrt's on June 4?

_____

7. How many hours of work will Gerry get in during this week?

_____

8. If Willy earns $3.00 an hour at Myrt's, how much will he earn during this week?

_____

DIRECTIONS Read about George's class trip.

George's class has been studying space explorations. They've planned a trip to the Kennedy Space Center and Cape Canaveral Air Force Station. To make the most of their two days, the group obtained a schedule of events at the two sites.

After careful planning, the class decided to begin their first day by taking the earliest possible bus tour of the Space Center. Then they plan to see the next appearance of "The Spaceman" before grabbing a quick lunch. After lunch the group plans to split up, with each group catching two of the six space movies of their choice. This should take about two hours in all. Then they have a reservation which their teacher has kept a secret. She'd covered that portion of the schedule. All George and his classmates know is that this activity had to be previously arranged for 3:30.

After the Secret Mission, as George's teacher called it, the group would have dinner at the Orbit Cafeteria, depending on the time.

The plans for the second day were not quite as carefully laid out, since they weren't sure how much they'd get done the first day. They were definitely going to take in the Air Force Station and visit the Gallery of Spaceflight. Their teacher had said they'd most likely want to return to the secret activity on their second day and then, if time permitted, anyone who chose to could

shop in the Gift Gantry and visit the Galaxy Center.

George's teacher asked the students to bring their own money for meals and souvenirs. She said that any other costs would be covered by the fund raiser they'd had as a class project earlier in the year.

Study the schedule of events George and his classmates used to plan their two-day trip. Use the story and the schedule as you answer the questions.

TODAY'S SCHEDULE OF EVENTS

Bus Tours	Exploration Station	Theater 2	Free Guided Tour of Exhibits	The 'Spaceman'	Spaceport USA
Approximately Two Hours Each	Aerospace Activities For School-Age Kids	Six Different Space Movies 15– 30 Minutes Each	30 Minutes Each Starting at the Information Counter	10:30–11:30 12:00– 1:00 1:30– 2:30 3:00– 4:00	Open from 8:00 to 6:00
RED TOUR: VISIT KENNEDY SPACE CENTER Incl. THE SPACE SHUTTLE LAUNCH AREA Continuous Departures 9:30 until 3:30	Available To Educational Groups By Prior Reservation Only	9:05 9:40 10:05 10:40 11:05 11:40 12:05 12:40 1:05 1:40 2:05 2:40 3:05 3:40 4:05 4:40	11:15 12:30 1:15 2:15 3:00	Get your picture with our "Spaceman". Find him somewhere in Spaceport Central at above times	**Gift Gantry** Film & Souvenirs Open from 8:45 to 5:45 **Orbit Cafeteria** Open from 8:00 to 5:00 Variety Menu
BLUE TOUR: VISIT THE HISTORIC CAPE CANAVERAL AIR FORCE STATION Ask For Departure Times	Open For Family Groups At Times Posted On Schedule Board				**Galaxy Center** Theaters and Exhibits Open daily 8:00 to 5:45
★ ★ ★ ★ ★ Ticket Counter Opens 8:15 ★ ★ ★ ★ ★ Bus Tour Rates Adult $4.00 Child 1.75					**Outdoor Shops** Ice Cream, Popcorn Drinks and Snacks Open from Mid-Morning to early Evening
	NO CHARGE FOR THEATERS				**Gallery of Spaceflight** Open from 8:00 to 5:45

1. Which bus tour will the group take upon their arrival on their first day?

   _____

2. Approximately what time will the first day's bus tour end?

   _____

3. What time does the Gallery of Spaceflight close?

   _____

4. Where will the students go for the "Secret Mission"?

   _____

5. What is the maximum time the students should allow for the free guided tour?

   _____

6. Where will the students be able to purchase a memento of their trip to take home?

   _____

REMEMBER Look for key words when reading a schedule.

Maps and More

Where might you begin to look for a map and any other information about a new place you're about to visit? In this lesson, you will learn about using a reference book that is just the place to look.

 KEYS to Using an Atlas

An atlas is a book of maps and other information about places.

LEARN   An atlas is a reference book of maps and other information about one or many countries. Real things are represented on the maps by *symbols* which are explained in a *key* or *legend*. A compass symbol shows the directions.

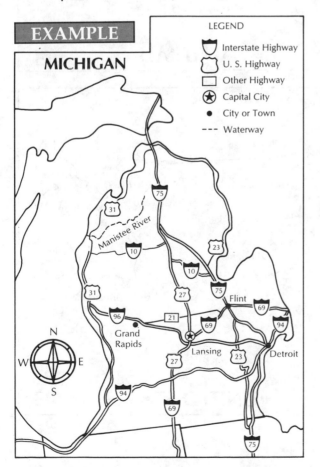

EXAMPLE

MICHIGAN

LEGEND
- Interstate Highway
- U. S. Highway
- Other Highway
- ★ Capital City
- ● City or Town
- --- Waterway

DIRECTIONS Use the map to complete each sentence.

1. The Manistee River is found in the

   _____ part of

   Michigan.

2. You'd travel through _____ on Interstate 96 from Detroit to Grand Rapids.

3. The city of _____ can be reached by highways 69, 23, 21, or 75.

4. The capital of Michigan is

   _____ .

② Practice Using an Atlas

DIRECTIONS Every city shown on a map in an atlas is listed alphabetically in the index by page number and by a letter followed by a number. Guide letters are down the side of a map and guide numbers are across the top or bottom. To find a city coded as *D4* in the index, you go across the map from *D* and stop under the number 4. The city will be found *near* that point. Use the maps to complete the index entries below.

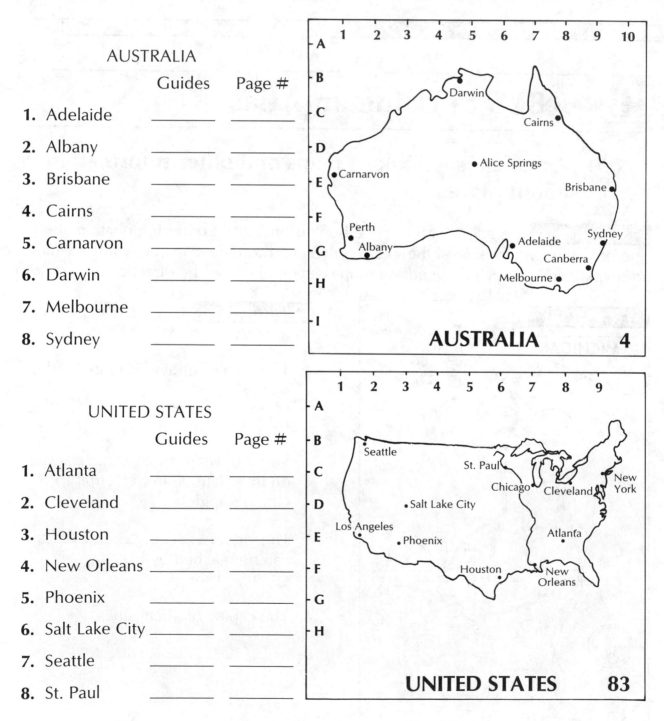

AUSTRALIA

	Guides	Page #
1. Adelaide		
2. Albany		
3. Brisbane		
4. Cairns		
5. Carnarvon		
6. Darwin		
7. Melbourne		
8. Sydney		

UNITED STATES

	Guides	Page #
1. Atlanta		
2. Cleveland		
3. Houston		
4. New Orleans		
5. Phoenix		
6. Salt Lake City		
7. Seattle		
8. St. Paul		

3 Read and Apply

DIRECTIONS An atlas may also include a brief description of a country or city to give the reader a better idea of what an area is like. Read about the city of Charleston, South Carolina and the continent of Africa.

Charleston, an important Atlantic seaport and the second largest city in South Carolina, boasts well-preseved old homes and buildings from the 1700s and 1800s. The people of Charleston have preserved some of the country's oldest landscaped gardens. The birthplace of the Confederacy in 1861, Charleston was founded by English and British West Indies settlers in 1670. The city, named for King Charles II of England, was originally called Charles Town until its present name was adopted in 1783. The January temperatures in Charleston range from 44 to 59°F with a humid 75 to 88°F in July. Among the many historical sights to see are the Edmonston-Alston House, the Hunley Museum, the Heyward-Washington House, the Old Slave Mart Museum and Gallery, the Magnolia Plantation, the Cypress Gardens, and the Yorktown Carrier.

Africa, richest of all the continents in its variety of wildlife, is also blessed with abundant and varied vegetation. The tropical rain forest stretches from the Gulf of Guinea in the western part of the country to the eastern highlands of the Great Rift Valley. There is evidence that the northern and southern boundaries of the rain forest once extended much further before being replaced by the grassy savanna. The savanna, a favorite of tourists, is home of the world's great herds and their enemies, the cats. It is also home to scavenging dogs and other vultures. Deserts to the north and south of the savanna, the Sahara, the Namib, and the Kalahari, house life which survive where no man could. African lakes are filled with crocodiles and, where more shallow, flamingoes. Rivers, swamps, and mountainous highlands are also found in this vast continent.

An atlas often contains tables and lists of information. Read the atlas information and then answer the questions below.

Largest Countries of the World in Area			
Country	Area (sq. mi.)	Country	Area (sq. mi.)
1. Soviet Union	8,600,350	6. Australia	2,967,909
2. Canada	3,851,809	7. India	1,229,210
3. China	3,691,500	8. Argentina	1,072,162
4. United States	3,675,545	9. Sudan	967,500
5. Brazil	3,286,487	10. Algeria	919,595

Temperature Extremes and Elevation

■ The highest temperature ever recorded in the United States was 137°F at Greenland Ranch, Death Valley, California on July 10, 1913.

■ The lowest temperature ever recorded in the United States was −76°F at Tanana, Alaska in January, 1886.

■ The highest elevation in the United States is Mount McKinley, Alaska at 20,320 feet.

■ The lowest elevation in the United States is in Death Valley, California at 282 feet below sea level.

■ The average elevation of the United States is 2,500 feet.

1. Where is the lowest point in the United States?

_____

2. What is the third largest country in size?

_____

3. What is the square mileage of the United States?

_____

4. What are the highest and lowest temperatures ever recorded in the United States?

_____ and _____

5. What two countries are smaller in size than Argentina?

_____ and

_____

6. What two records are held by Death Valley, California?

_____ and

_____

7. What is the largest country in the world in area?

_____

Not Just Trivia

Where can you turn if you need a friend's zip code to mail a letter or if your hamster bites you and you're not sure if first aid is needed. In this lesson, you'll learn about a reference book that contains these answers and more.

1 KEYS to Using an Almanac

An almanac contains useful facts.

LEARN   An *almanac* is a reference book containing interesting and useful facts. General almanacs span a wide range of subject areas, while special almanacs pertain to topics such as sports or farming. An almanac may have a brief index for quick reference, in addition to a general index listing the contents in detail. Just as in other reference books, facts in an almanac's index may be found under several different subject headings.

EXAMPLE   Facts about the sun may be found under *sun, solar system, solar day, calendars, astronomy, planets,* and perhaps even more topics.

DIRECTIONS Write two or more subject areas under which you might look in an index for information on each topic.

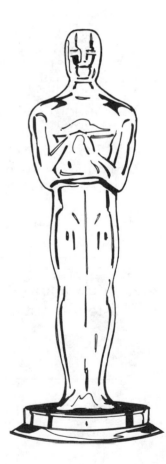

1. Gold _____

2. Roman Numerals _____

3. Football _____

4. Presidents _____

5. Academy awards _____

2 Practice With Almanacs

DIRECTIONS Use the quick reference index from an almanac to complete the work below. Write the subject *and* page numbers where you'd look to find the information.

QUICK REFERENCE INDEX

ACTORS AND ACTRESSES 399–415
AEROSPACE 168–174
ANIMALS 152–156
AREA CODES, TELEPHONE 229–257
ARTS AND MEDIA 364–375
BASKETBALL 807–816
BOOKS, BEST SELLERS 367–368
BUILDINGS, TALL 684–689
CALENDARS . . . 342–344, 724–735, 738–742
CITIES OF NORTH AMERICA . . 82, 673–683
COLLEGES AND UNIVERSITIES 183–209
CONGRESSIONAL ELECTIONS . . . 39, 40–48
CONSTITUTION 443–450
CONSUMER SURVIVAL KIT 56–114
COPYRIGHT LAW 767–768
CRIME 782–786
DECLARATION OF
INDEPENDENCE 441–442, 451
DISASTERS 754–762
DRUGS, ABUSED 36–38, 83–85
EDUCATION 93–95, 142–148
ENVIRONMENT 149–157
FIRST AID 88–89
FLAGS OF THE WORLD (COLOR) . 457–461
FOOTBALL 824–842
GOVERNORS 48, 51, 324–327
HEADS OF STATE 545–633
HEIGHT AND WEIGHT AVERAGES 774
HISTORY 473–514

INDEX, GENERAL 3–32
INVENTIONS AND DISCOVERIES . . 763–767
MAPS (COLOR) 462–472
METEOROLOGICAL DATA 745–753
METRIC SYSTEM 693–697
NATIONAL PARKS 436–439
NATIONS OF THE WORLD 545–634
NUTRITION 90–92
OFF-BEAT NEWS STORIES 924–925
OLYMPICS 787–798
PERSONALITIES, NOTED 376–416
POPULATION, U.S. 217–274
    WORLD 634–635
PRESIDENTS, U.S. 308, 524–531
SCIENTIFIC ACHIEVEMENTS AND
DISCOVERIES 921–922
SPORTS 787–885
STATES OF THE UNION 644–672
TELEVISION 96–97, 372–373
THEATER, RECORDINGS, FILMS . . . 364–367
UNITED NATIONS 641–643
U.S. FACTS 431–440
U.S. GOVERNMENT 317–328
VITAL STATISTICS 769–786
WEIGHTS AND MEASURES 94, 693–700
WORLD FACTS 532–544
WORLD HISTORY 487–514
ZIP CODES 229–257

1. You want to find out what day of the week you were born.

_____

_____

2. You want to read about major disasters in history.

_____

_____

3. You'd like to read some weird news stories.

_____

_____

4. You want to identify an unfamiliar flag you saw.

_____

_____

5. You want to read about discoveries in science.

_____

_____

6. You're wondering if your size is average for your age.

_____

_____

DIRECTIONS   Read Nick's letter to his friend.

Dear Tyler,

I've just discovered the best book and think you'll want to know about it, if you don't already! You know how you and I love to play all the trivia games. <u>This</u> book has all the answers, or at least a lot of them!

First, I have to tell you how I stumbled onto it. I'd been wondering about several facts I didn't know the last time I played a trivia game, plus I needed your zip code so I could write you.

Well, I stopped off at the library yesterday, and the librarian must have thought I looked really confused. She came over and asked what I needed, and I rattled off several things, none of which was related in any way. I probably sounded "spacey"! Anyway, she handed me this thick book and said I'd find all those things including your zip code. No way, I thought! How could one book have all those crazy trivia answers and zip codes, too! Was I ever surprised!

By the way, I'll bet you don't know how many stripes identify a navy admiral, or who won the Super Bowl in 1983, or when balloons were invented.

I found every answer in that book <u>plus</u> your zip code, as you can see! Of course you know your zip code, but don't even dream that I'm going to tell you all the other answers! You'll have to find out on your own and let me know. Hope you're enjoying your new house.

Your friend,
Nick

P.S. The book, by the way, is an almanac. Check it out.

1. The odds against throwing two dice for a sum of 7 are 5 to 1.
2. The well-known poet, Shel Silverstein, was born in 1932.
3. Lyndon Baines Johnson became president of the United States in 1963 when John Fitzgerald Kennedy was assassinated.
4. The abbreviation for Connecticut is *CT*.
5. On April 14, 1912, the Titanic sank in the North Atlantic.
6. There are twenty-seven zeroes in the number, one octillion.
7. The first black person to win the Nobel Peace Prize was Dr. Ralph Bunche in 1950.
8. The movie *Star Wars* was second to *E.T. The Extra Terrestrial* as the most often rented video movie in 1986.
9. In 1986, farms in the United States raised 105,468,000 dairy and beef cattle.
10. Montreal defeated Calgary to become the Stanley Cup Champions in 1986 hockey competition.
11. Delaware, the first state in the union, celebrated its 200th year of statehood in 1987.
12. The University of Notre Dame was founded in 1842 in Notre Dame, Indiana near South Bend.
13. Daily consumption of 50 milligrams of vitamin C and 1200 milligrams of calcium are recommended for an eleven-year-old who weighs 99 to 101 pounds.
14. The light heavyweight champion boxer in 1983 was Michael Spinks.

Noted Personalities _____

Weights and Measures and Numbers _____

Presidents, Vice Presidents _____

Postal Information _____

Sports _____

Disasters _____

Arts and Media _____

Agriculture _____

Historical Anniversaries _____

Education _____

Nutrition _____

REMEMBER You'll find facts, facts, and more facts in an almanac.

A Wealth of Information

What houses all the knowledge in the world? In this lesson, you'll read about a "knowledge bank" that stores all the written and spoken information available since time began.

1 KEYS to Using the Library

A library is a wealth of information.

LEARN The history and culture of a society are preserved in written and spoken words. This wealth of information is housed in a library. The word *library* comes from a Latin word meaning *book,* since libraries were originally large collections of books. Today, in addition to books, libraries contain periodicals or magazines, newspapers, records, tapes, films, and other sources of information.

DIRECTIONS Answer the questions in your own words.

1. What is a periodical? _____

2. How did a library get its name? _____

   _____

3. Why is it important to preserve a society's history and culture? _____

   _____

4. How have libraries changed over time? _____

   _____

   _____

Using a Library **177**

Practice Using the Library

DIRECTIONS A book may tell of an *actual* or *imaginary* happening. Books of actual, or real, events are called *non-fiction,* while books of imaginary events are called *fiction.* Fiction books are housed together and shelved alphabetically by the first letter of the author's last name. The *Dewey Decimal System* is used in most libraries to classify non-fiction books. Study the categories and examples of the Dewey Decimal System. Then read each sentence about non-fiction books, and write the appropriate Dewey Decimal System classification numbers on the line. The first one is done for you.

000–099 General (encyclopedias, computer books)

100–199 Philosophy (dreams, self-help)

200–299 Religion (mythology, religion)

300–399 Social Sciences (costumes, money, manners, fairy tales)

400–499 Language (dictionaries, words, languages)

500–599 Sciences (animals, mathematics, plants)

600–699 Technology (human body, gardening, cooking, airplanes)

700–799 Arts (photography, sports, games, crafts, music, art)

800–899 Literature (poetry, plays, jokes)

900–999 Geography and History (atlases, history, geography)

1. Pat Tung's book tells how to prepare Chinese foods.
600–699

2. We'll need to take an atlas on our trip.

3. *Word Origins and Their Romantic Stories* is a fascinating book about how things got their names.

4. My little brother loves to read about dinosaurs and other prehistoric animals.

5. Our class is studying plays before we write our own.

6. My friend knows the story of every character in Greek and Roman mythology.

7. My dad is always reading books about money.

8. This book has super tips for using my new computer.

DIRECTIONS Read about some reference materials available to you.

The reference section of a library contains familiar encyclopedias with information on almost any subject. Often, however, you may want to consult a specialized encyclopedia about a particular topic. *Lands and Peoples* is a set of specialized encyclopedias which give detailed information about different countries and their people. *About the Author* is an autobiographical series containing the life stories of authors written by the authors themselves. *Something About the Author,* on the other hand, includes biographical information on the lives of authors written by others. The *Science and Technology* encyclopedias contain in-depth information about matters of science and the development of new ideas and processes. In our ever-changing world, you may find encyclopedic materials called *Up To Date Information On Countries* listing the most current information, some of which is so recent that it is not yet bound in book form. Another series of books contains all there is to know about states in the United States, including state names, seals, flags, flowers, songs, etc.

The reference section is also where you will find atlases, almanacs, phone books, thesauruses of synonyms and antonyms, and common and specialized dictionaries such as dictionaries of rhyming words. In addition, shelves in the reference section may have a number of other special books and index books listing the books available on specific topics. *Sports Books for Children, The Children's Guide to Periodicals, Adventure Books, Science Fair Projects, American Nicknames, Rules of the Game, Children's Television, Military Aircraft* and *Facts About the Presidents* are a few of these specialized books.

1. *The World Almanac & Book of Facts*
2. *The Modern Rhyming Dictionary*
3. *Roget's Thesaurus*
4. *Science and Technology*
5. *Children's Guide to Periodicals*
6. *Something About the Author*
7. *Lands and Peoples*
8. *Children's Television*
9. *Science Fair Projects*
10. *Up to Date Information on Countries*
11. *American Nicknames*
12. *Rules of the Game*
13. *Military Aircraft*
14. *Adventure Books*
15. *Sports Books for Children*

1. Emil's class is having a science fair. Emil wants to come up with a project that deals with a current discovery in science. He's looked in many science books and still doesn't have an idea.

   _____

2. Sophie loves to write poems but sometimes finds herself at a loss for synonyms and word pairs that rhyme. She feels her specialty is in writing poems about real things, but she'd like to try writing adven-

ture, also. She thinks she might get inspiration from reading about some of her favorite poets.

   _____

3. Michelle wants to be an astronaut some day, so she tries to keep abreast of the latest discoveries. She loves airplanes and hopes to go to the Air Force Academy prior to pursuing a career in space.

   _____

4. Eddie considers himself an expert in sports and games trivia. He knows, however, that there are always more facts to be learned. That's why he can often be found in the reference section of the library.

   _____

5. Although Gracie realizes there may not be much information available, she wants to do her report on a tiny country in Africa. She read about it in the newspaper and, since it's been in the news recently, she hopes to find some new magazine articles.

   _____

REMEMBER You can find any information you need in the library.

Help Yourself in the Library

You desperately need some books to begin your report. You go into the library, only to find the librarian is busy with a story-hour group. Can you help yourself? In this lesson, you'll learn where to begin and how to use three clues to find all the books you need.

1 KEYS to the Card Catalog

The card catalog contains three different cards for each book.

LEARN If you know the *subject* of a fiction or non-fiction book, its *author,* or its *title,* you can find a card for the book in the card catalog of a library. The three cards are filed alphabetically by the author's last name, the subject, or the title with the title card filed by the first main word. A juvenile fiction book has a *J* above the author's last initial.

EXAMPLE *The 18th Emergency,* an adventure story by Betsy Byars, would have a *subject* card filed under *A* for *adventure,* an *author* card under *B* for *Byars,* and a *title* card under *E* for *eighteenth.*

DIRECTIONS Write the letter of the card catalog drawer where you'd find a card for each book.

1. James Lowe's adventure book, *The Celery Stalks at Midnight:*

subject _____   author _____   title _____

2. *Bubbles,* a collection of poems edited by Theodore E. Wade, Jr.:

subject _____   author _____   title _____

2 Practice With the Card Catalog

DIRECTIONS The topic is first on the subject card, while the title of the book comes first on the title card. The author's name is listed first on the author card. The *call numbers* on the left tell that the book is a non-fiction book that can be found in the shelves where the 600 books on sports are located. The *J* tells that the book is a *juvenile* book. The author's last name begins with an *N.* Bison published the 93 page book in 1983. A subject card can be found in the *C* drawer of the card catalog for *cars* or for *Corvette,* and there may also be a subject card for this book in the *S* drawer for *sports.* Use the author, title, and subject cards to answer the questions below.

SUBJECT CARD

J	Cars—sports
629.22	Nichols, Richard
N	The Classic Corvette
	Bison (1983)
	93 pp.

TITLE CARD

J	The Classic Corvette
629.22	Nichols, Richard
N	Bison (1983)
	93 pp.

AUTHOR CARD

J	Nichols, Richard
629.22	The Classic Corvette
N	Bison (1983)
	93 pp.

1. Which of the cards would be found in the *C* drawer of the card catalog?

_____

Why?

_____

_____

_____

2. Why isn't the author's name listed first on some of the cards?

_____

_____

3. What letter would be on the drawer of the card catalog for each of the cards?
   subject _____ or _____
   author _____   title _____

4. What does the call number tell about the book?

_____

_____

5. What does *J* above the call number mean?

_____

Read and Apply

DIRECTIONS There may be many copies of a book's subject card in the card catalog, since the book may be listed under several different topics. Doris Faber's biography, *Robert Frost: America's Poet* would have subject cards under *P* for *poet* or *poetry,* *B* for *biography,* and possibly several other subject cards for some of Frost's famous poems. Read each sentence and circle *all* the subjects where you might look in the card catalog to find a subject card for helpful books.

1. You're doing a report on the Civil War.

    wars   Civil War   1800's   computers   Lincoln

2. You want to learn about constructing model airplanes.

    crafts   food   airplanes   models   hobbies

3. You need a book of recipes for foods from France.

    food   recipes   cooking   France   cookbooks

4. You want to find a book you once read about baseball's Babe Ruth.

    candy   sports   baseball   major leagues   cars

5. You want to learn about hibernating animals.

    alligators   reptiles   cats   hibernation   bears

6. You want to read the Declaration of Independence.

    World War I   Revolutionary War   Independence Day   history

7. You want to prepare yourself before getting braces at the dentist.

    dentistry   crutches   dental hygiene   teeth   orthodontics

DIRECTIONS Write possible subject areas where you might look in the card catalog for books about these topics. The first one is done for you.

1. quilting Colonial Times, needlework, sewing, crafts

2. ships _____

3. labrador retriever _____

4. Harvard University _____

5. Communist countries _____

6. astronauts _____

7. costumes _____

DIRECTIONS Read each card from a card catalog. Write *subject, title,* or *author* on the line above the card's contents to tell which kind of card is shown. Then complete the sentences below by circling the best answer in parentheses.

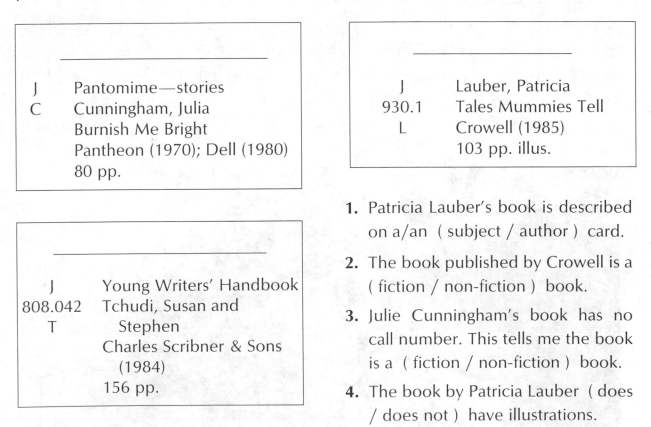

J C Pantomime—stories
Cunningham, Julia
Burnish Me Bright
Pantheon (1970); Dell (1980)
80 pp.

J 930.1 L Lauber, Patricia
Tales Mummies Tell
Crowell (1985)
103 pp. illus.

J 808.042 T Young Writers' Handbook
Tchudi, Susan and Stephen
Charles Scribner & Sons (1984)
156 pp.

1. Patricia Lauber's book is described on a/an (subject / author) card.

2. The book published by Crowell is a (fiction / non-fiction) book.

3. Julie Cunningham's book has no call number. This tells me the book is a (fiction / non-fiction) book.

4. The book by Patricia Lauber (does / does not) have illustrations.

REMEMBER Look for a subject, title, or author card in the card catalog.

China's Great Wall

Remembering details from your reading can be difficult without good notes. In this lesson, you'll learn about notetaking as you read about the Great Wall of China.

---

 1 KEYS to Notetaking

Notes are the main words of ideas and details.

LEARN You take notes to help you remember ideas and details you read. First, select an important idea or detail. Then write an important word or a phrase in your own words to summarize that information. Notes should be brief, omitting all unnecessary or unimportant words.

Information: The *Great Wall* provided *little protection* to *China* during *major invasions*.

Notes: China's Great Wall—no real help in big battles

DIRECTIONS Underline the important words in each sentence. Put an *X* before the words or phrase that represents the best notetaking.

1. The Great Wall is a major tourist attraction today.

   _____Great Wall—many tourists

   _____The Great Wall—attracts many tourists today

   _____Many people go to see the Great Wall.

2. The first portions of the Great Wall were constructed around 400 B.C.

   _____Great Wall—first parts were built around 400 B.C.

   _____Great Wall—begun around 400 B.C.

   _____The Great Wall construction began around 400 B.C.

Practice With Notetaking

2

DIRECTIONS When selecting main ideas for notetaking, it is helpful to seek brief answers to the basic questions *who or what, when, why, how,* and *where*. Read the paragraph and use the underlined words to answer the questions. The first one is done for you.

The <u>Great Wall</u> of China is the longest structure in the world. It was built totally <u>by hand</u> over a period of some 2,000 years from <u>400 B.C.</u> through <u>1600 A.D.</u> The wall extends across <u>northern China</u> between northcentral China to the east coast. The wall was constructed for <u>protection</u> from northern invasions.

A. Who or what? _Great Wall_

B. When? _____

C. Why? _____

D. How? _____

E. Where? _____

DIRECTIONS After noting the main ideas, take notes of some details about each main idea. A good way to expand or tell more about a main idea is to ask the same question again. For example, "Who or what is the Great Wall?" A good answer would be that it is the Great Wall *of China*. Continue asking the same question until you have all the information or what you need. Record your first answer after each lettered question below. Then refer to the original paragraph to add additional notes about each idea. (You'll notice that some main ideas from the paragraph have more details than others and one has none. More details could be added if additional information were included.) The first one is done for you.

A. Who or what? _Great Wall_

Who or what? _of China_

Who or what? _longest structure in_

world

B. When? _____

_____

When? _____

C. Why? _____

_____

Why? _____

_____

D. How? _____

E. Where? _____

_____

Where? _____

_____

Read and Apply

DIRECTIONS Read more about notetaking.

How notes are written and organized depends largely on you and your needs. As details are compiled, notes can, and often do, become extensive. For this and other reasons, some notetakers prefer to use a separate note card for each main idea.

You may use numbers, letters, asterisks, hyphens, slashes, arrows, or other marks to separate or highlight information. It helps to use these marks consistently so that when you see an asterisk, for instance, you can remember that the notation identifies a main idea, a measurement, or whatever. The use of a hyphen can be helpful to mean *to* or *through* such as in *400 B.C.–1600 A.D.* or to precede details. A slash is often used between synonyms or similar ideas such as *tourists/visitors* if you want to remember two or more possible words you could

use. Arrows can be used to show cause and effect or other kinds of relationships. For example, you may write *Great Wall → protection* to note that the wall was built for protection.

Notes may also take the form of a list, chart, table, diagram, etc. A list of notes including several dates and events may be organized into a chart. If notes consist of numerous figures or symbols such as Chinese words or measurement statistics of the Great Wall, these pieces of information may be best suited to a table.

Once notes are written, organize them in a meaningful way. Although note cards provide for easy organization, a notetaker may choose to "cut and paste," cutting notes apart and placing them in order on another sheet of paper.

Read the article. Then use what you've learned about notetaking to complete the notes in their various forms below. Write the important words on the lines.

China was once ruled by an emperor who desired to end the invasion by Nomads living north of the Yellow Plain. In around 400 B.C., the ruler ordered that a gigantic wall be erected. New parts were built in 221 B.C. by the Ch'in dynasty, in 202 B.C. by the Han dynasty, and in 581 A.D. by Sui.

The wall stands 25 feet high and narrows in width from a 25-foot base to 15 feet across the top. Forty-foot high watchtowers are every 120 to 200 yards all along the wall.

Most of the Great Wall is still standing, though sections were destroyed and rebuilt over the years. The wall that is seen today is credited to the Ming dynasty of the late 1300's through the middle 1600's. Some of the present wall was reconstructed as recently as 1949.

Although the Chinese do not use the Great Wall for defense today, it does produce much revenue for the country, as tourists spend their money while visiting. The famous wall also lends itself to research as scientists study the effects of earthquakes on the wall's structure.

1. ■ Past Use

   _____

   ■ Present Use

   _____

   _____

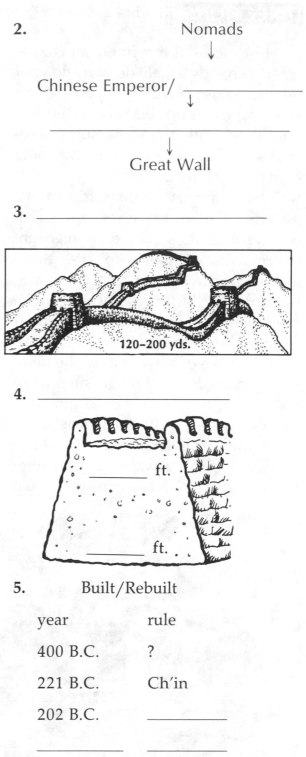

2.   Nomads
                                  ↓
   Chinese Emperor/ _____
                                  ↓
   _____
                                  ↓
                            Great Wall

3. _____

   120–200 yds.

4. _____

   _____ ft.

   _____ ft.

5.   Built/Rebuilt

   year   rule

   400 B.C.   ?

   221 B.C.   Ch'in

   202 B.C.   _____

   _____   _____

   1300's A.D.   _____

Make your notes brief and easy to understand.

Wonders of the World

Seven seems to be a popular number when listing wonders of the world. In this lesson, you'll learn about outlining as you read about three different lists of wonders of the world.

KEYS to Outlining

Outlining is organizing important information in a special way.

LEARN In an outline, main ideas are preceded by *Roman Numerals, subtopics* begin with *capital letters,* and details follow *Arabic numerals.*

I. Modern Wonders of the World
    A. Human-made
        1. Suez Canal in Egypt
        2. Alcan Highway in Alaska
        3. Atomic Energy Research Establishment in England
        4. Dneproges Dam in Russia
        5. Eiffel Tower in Paris
        6. Empire State Building in New York City
        7. Golden Gate Bridge in San Francisco

DIRECTIONS Use the outline above to complete the sentences.

1. The main idea of the outline is _____

_____ .

2. There are _____ details under the subtopic.

3. The subtopic is _____ .

Practice Outlining

DIRECTIONS Read about some wonders of the modern world. Fill in the outline.

One of the seven natural wonders of the world is the Great Barrier Reef, which stretches for some 1,250 miles along the northeastern part of Australia. Scientists are worried about the future of the world's largest coral formation. For the past twenty years, starfish have been feeding on the living part of the reef. Without this new growth, the reef's existence is greatly endangered.

Another of the natural wonders is the Grand Canyon, which engulfs the Colorado River in northwest Arizona.

The canyon, formed by the river over millions of years, displays many different rock formations in every shade and color. Wide variations in elevation and temperatures in the canyon create environments perfect for a wide variety of wildlife.

Spectacular in their own right are the human-made wonders of the world. Built in 1889 for an exposition, the Eiffel Tower in Paris rises 984 feet with a 330-feet base. The tower was, for years, the world's tallest structure.

I. _____

    A. Great Barrier Reef _____

        1. _____

        2. _____

        3. _____

    B. _____

        1. Engulfs Colorado River _____

        2. _____

        3. _____

II. Human-Made Wonders _____

    A. _____

        1. _____

        2. Once world's tallest structure _____

        3. _____

DIRECTIONS Read about the Seven Wonders of the Ancient World.

Long ago the Greeks and Romans felt that seven objects made by humans were noteworthy. The Colossus of Rhodes stood near the Aegean Sea off the coast of the island of Rhodes. Honoring Helios, the sun god, the hollow bronze statue stood about 120 feet tall. Built around 200 B.C. over a period of twelve years, it was destroyed by an earthquake shortly after its unveiling, and only pieces remain.

King Nebuchadnezzar II, who ruled Babylon around 600 B.C., had the Hanging Gardens of Babylon erected near Baghdad in Iraq for one of his wives. The gardens are now gone but old writings tell of their remarkable size. The brick walls around Babylon are generally included in this "wonder," since their width allowed two chariots to travel side by side on top.

Phidias, a Greek sculptor, created the Statue of Zeus at Olympia, Greece around 435 B.C. In honor of Zeus, king of the gods, the statue once stood 40 feet high, with Zeus's clothes made of gold and his skin of ivory.

The oldest and most well-preserved of the ancient wonders are the Pyramids of Egypt which were tombs for Egyptian kings. The Temple of Artemis at Ephesus was built around 550 B.C. in what is now Turkey. Although the marble, tile, and wooden temple burned some 200 years later and a second one also burned, the foundations remain.

Pieces of marble remain from the Mausoleum at Halicarnassus, erected as a tomb for Mausolus, a government leader in Persia. The building was so magnificent that all large tombs are now called mausoleums. In Alexandria, Egypt, a 440 foot lighthouse once stood until destroyed by two different earthquakes. Soldiers fought from the fortress at the base, as a bonfire burned continuously at the tower's peak.

Use information from the article you just read to complete the outline below.

Wonders of the Ancient World

I. Colossus of Rhodes
   A. Construction

       1. _____

          _____

       2. _____

          _____

   B. Destruction

       1. _____

          _____

       2. _____

          _____

II. _____

       _____

   A. Erected in Iraq
      1. Near Baghdad

      2. _____

         _____

   B. Walls around Babylon

      1. _____

         _____

      2. _____

         _____

III. Statue of Zeus
   A. In Olympia, Greece

   B. _____

      _____

IV. Mausoleum at Halicarnassus

   A. _____

      _____

   B. _____

      _____

V. _____

   A. Tombs for Egyptian Kings

   B. _____

      _____

VI. Lighthouse of Alexandria

   A. _____

      _____

   B. _____

      _____

VII. _____

      _____

   A. _____

      _____

   B. _____

      _____

REMEMBER Outlining organizes main ideas, subtopics, and details.

Remember the Alamo

Someone tells you a story worth repeating. When you repeat the story, though, you generally change it as you tell it in your own words. In this lesson, you'll learn about rewriting what you've read as you write information in your own words. You'll also read about the Alamo.

---

 1 ## KEYS to Paraphrasing

Paraphrasing is writing something in your own words.

LEARN To paraphrase something you read, rewrite it in your own words by using synonyms for main words and by rearranging the information.

EXAMPLE Original: Although all the Texans lost their lives at the Alamo, the famous battle is remembered as an heroic one. Paraphrased: The historic battle of the Alamo is often cited as an example of bravery, despite the total loss of defenders.

The word *historic* is substituted for the words *remembered* and *famous,* and *Texans who fought* are called *defenders.* The information is also rearranged.

DIRECTIONS Read the pair of sentences. Circle the words in sentence *b* which are substitutes for the underlined words in sentence *a.*

a. The Alamo is a symbol of Texas' battle for indepedence.

b. Texans are remembered for their freedom fight at the Alamo.

2 Practice Paraphrasing

DIRECTIONS Read each numbered paragraph. Then read the three paragraphs that follow. Circle the letters of the two paragraphs that best paraphrase the original. Cross out the letter of the paragraph that is too much like the original.

1. The Alamo was constructed as a monastery and church around 1718 in the city of San Antonio, Texas. The high walls around the structure prompted its occasional use as a fort.

   a. The Alamo, although built for religious purposes, was sometimes used as a fort. Built around 1718, the Alamo stood inside protective walls in San Antonio, Texas.

   b. The Alamo was built in 1718 as a church and monastery in San Antonio, Texas. The high walls around the building caused its occasional use as a fort.

   c. The Alamo was built around 1718 in San Antonio, Texas. It was actually built as a church but was sometimes used as a fort, since it was surrounded by walls.

2. In 1836, General Santa Anna and his 5,000 Mexican soldiers made a surprise attack on the Alamo with its 150 Texans. The battle lasted thirteen days before Santa Anna's troops scaled the walls to defeat the Texans.

   a. General Santa Anna and his men made a surprise attack on the Alamo in 1836. The battle lasted thirteen days and then Santa Anna's troops climbed over the walls to defeat the Texans.

   b. Surprised by the attack of General Santa Anna and his troop of 5,000 Mexican men, 150 Texans fought mightily for thirteen days in 1836 before being defeated when the invaders came over the walls.

   c. After thirteen days of battling, 150 Texans were defeated at the Alamo in 1836. The Mexican general, Santa Anna, and his 5,000 men ended their unexpected attack by climbing over the walls.

Read and Apply

DIRECTIONS Read about paraphrasing.

Although it may appear that an original article is stated perfectly, keep in mind that any written material can be rewritten in many ways. Think about a topic like the battle of the Alamo. This battle was fought only once and yet thousands of people have written about it. Those writers have taken the same battle fought at the same place at the same time in history by the same people and written about it in their own words. The difference lies in the words they used to relate the events.

Suppose you choose to write a report on the Alamo. You'll begin by reading what other writers have said. Then you'll choose three or four articles which you find most helpful. Next, choose excerpts from each article to use in your report. To copy another writer's words exactly would not make your report original, so think about how you can write the information in your own words.

A good way to do this is to read a paragraph or two. After you understand the main idea and a few details, write the information, using synonyms or groups of words in place of the exact words you read. Next, reread the original article and compare it to what you wrote, asking yourself if the infor-

mation is correct and complete. Make necessary changes before reading another selection you'll paraphrase.

You may need to reword your writing several times before you're done. When you read your finished report, you'll find that your use of paraphrasing has created an original article, different from any other.

Read each sentence and paraphrase it.

1. James Bowie and Davy Crockett were among the men fighting to defend the Alamo.

_____

_____

_____

_____

2. Some historians believe that Davy Crockett was killed at the Alamo.

_____

_____

_____

_____

3. Sam Houston organized Texans and others to surprise and defeat General Santa Anna a month after the Alamo disaster.

_____

_____

_____

_____

4. The Texans declared their independence when Santa Anna was defeated.

_____

_____

_____

_____

DIRECTIONS Read the paragraph and paraphrase the information.

The Texans used their muskets as clubs to combat Santa Anna's men as they came over the walls surrounding the Alamo. The Mexicans then proceeded to kill the remaining six defenders. The bravery shown at the Alamo and the heartless slaying prompted the phrase, "Remember the Alamo." The saying continues to be used today as a reminder of brave deeds and to stress the importance of continuing to try even when a task seems impossible.

_____

_____

_____

_____

_____

_____

_____

_____

REMEMBER Paraphrasing is rewriting information in your own words.

Amish Life

"Where do I begin?" you may think as you try to make sense of all your notes to write a report. In this lesson, you'll learn where to begin and how to proceed through each phase of writing a report. You'll also read about the Amish people.

 ## KEYS to Report Writing

A report is written from organized notes.

LEARN Notes need to be organized in a meaningful sequence before beginning to write a report. A helpful guideline for organization is to group notes into those which answer basic questions of *who or what, when, why, how,* and *where.* Notes for a report on the Amish might be grouped like this:

Who are the Amish? Description
When did the Amish begin? History
How do the Amish live? Customs, Education, Homes
Why do the Amish live as they do? Religion, Beliefs
Where do the Amish live? Geographic locations

DIRECTIONS Categorize each of the numbered note titles. Use the list of question words to write the correct letter on the line before each note title.

_____ **1.** Amish in Canada   **a.** who

_____ **2.** Amish Schools   **b.** when

_____ **3.** Early Amish   **c.** why

_____ **4.** Amish Farming   **d.** how

_____ **5.** Amish Values   **e.** where

_____ **6.** Amish in United States

2 Practice Report Writing

DIRECTIONS Once notes are organized into categories, it is helpful to combine them by making as many outline maps as needed to include all the important information. Notes from each basic question form main ideas, subtopics, and details. Read the notes from Richard's "how" category and complete the outline map.

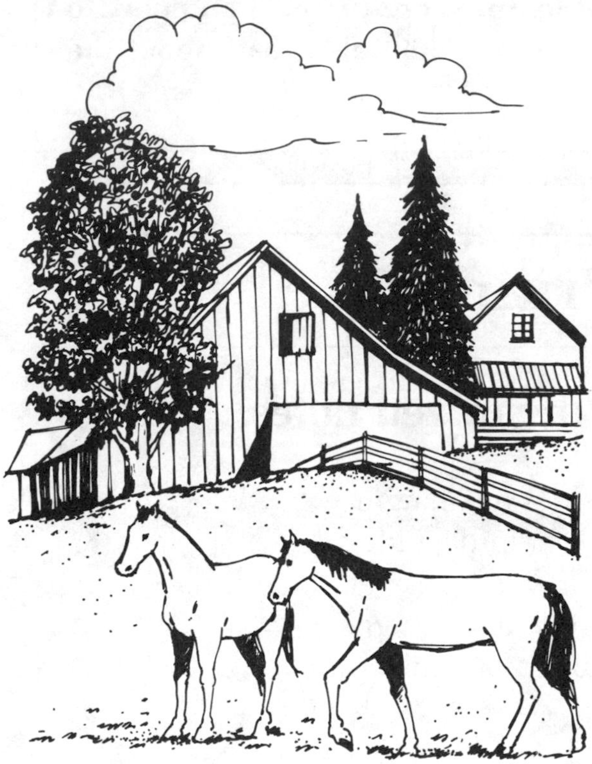

Amish Home

- *simple – not showy*
- *no curtains*
- *no pictures*

Amish Home

- *no electrical use*
- *farmhouse – typical*
- *"outside" kitchen*
- *kitchen sofa – father*
- *ice box with ice block*

LESSON 50, 198:

1. Outline Map

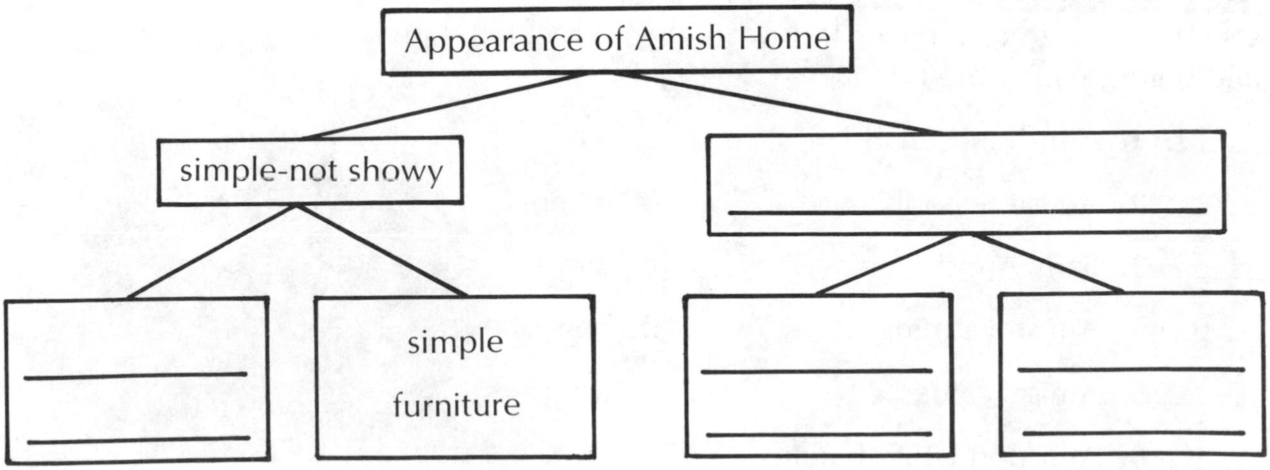

Appearance of Amish Home
simple-not showy
simple
furniture

DIRECTIONS Read the part of Richard's report about Amish homes and customs, written from his outline maps and notes. Notice that Richard used a main idea as his topic sentence to begin each paragraph. He used each of the subtopics and details to write sentences to support the main idea. Richard added his own thoughts to make his report more interesting and original.

1

The Amish home looks very different from the home where I live. Since the Amish choose a simple way of life to avoid showiness, there are no curtains at their windows and no pictures on the walls. That would sure make window washing and dusting easy on cleaning day! The home is probably a farmhouse, since those are typical Amish dwellings. The house is furnished with simple furniture, in keeping with simplicity. An Amish kitchen

2

often has an extension which is called an "outside" kitchen where extra things are stored. There are no electrical appliances like refrigerators, so foods that must be kept cold are kept in an icebox cooled by a block of ice.

Amish customs differ greatly from those that I have learned in my home. The men wear wide brimmed black hats and if they are married, they wear a beard. Women wear plain clothing with no jewelry or

3

cosmetics. Being farmers by choice and custom, the men use horses to operate their farm implements, all of which are simple tools like those used long ago. The family unit of father, mother, and children is highly valued in the Amish home. The parents strive for happy mealtimes which begin and end with prayer. The kitchen often has a couch or sofa where father rests after meals, while remaining close to the rest of the family. That's much like my family room and kitchen combined.

Read Richard's notes, outline map, and the beginning of the section of his report on Amish education. Then use his notes and outline map about Amish children's schooling to write a second paragraph.

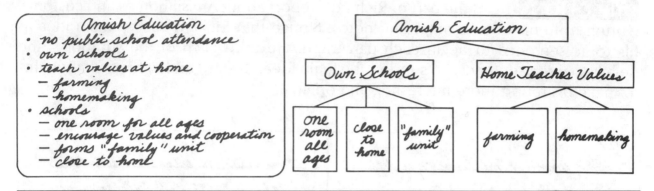

Amish Education
- no public school attendance
- own schools
- teach values at home
  - farming
  - homemaking
- schools
  - one room for all ages
  - encourage values and cooperation
  - forms "family" unit
  - close to home

> The Amish believe public school attendance would not help teach Amish values. For this reason, there are separate Amish schools close to the children's homes. The schools have one room for children of all ages. The Amish feel that this encourages cooperation among the children as they work together in a kind of "family" unit. The Amish home is another part of the educational system, since the home is where the children are taught how to be homemakers or farmers.

Amish Education
- Boys
  - school till eighth grade
  - then taught at home / farming
- Girls
  - school till eighth grade
  - then taught at home / homemaking and mothering

Amish Education
- Boys
  - through eighth grade
  - farming
- Girls
  - through eighth grade
  - homemaking and mothering

_____

_____

_____

_____

_____

REMEMBER Organizing notes into outline maps helps in report writing.

Getting Test-Wise

What can you do to prepare for a test besides study your book and notes from class? In this lesson, you'll learn about sharpening your test-taking skills.

---

1 KEYS to Taking Tests

Test questions may be in different forms.

LEARN You take tests to see which skills you can perform with ease and which skills need more of your concentration. Preparing for tests is essential, as is knowing how to take tests. Test questions may be presented in one form or a combination of these forms: *true-false, multiple choice, matching, sentence completion, essay.*

DIRECTIONS Write the name of the form of the question on the line. Then complete each question by writing or circling the answer.

_____ **1.** There are _____ different forms of test questions.

_____ **2.** Which is essential for taking a test?
   a. borrowing books from the library
   b. sleeping late on the morning of the test
   c. knowing how to take tests

_____ **3.** Discuss why tests are given. _____

_____

_____

_____ **4.** Test questions are always in one form.   T   F

DIRECTIONS Read each paragraph about a form of test question. Then complete the question or statement.

A. Multiple-choice questions usually offer from two to five possible answers. One answer may be a combination of others or "all of the above," which is correct only if the other choices are correct. The key is to eliminate incorrect choices, one at a time.

1. A multiple-choice question
   a. usually has two to five choices.
   b. may have only one correct answer.
   c. may have several correct answers.
   d. all of the above.

B. An essay question asks you to write an answer in your own words, which may include your opinions and conclusions. Those who enjoy discussing issues, usually like essay questions.

1. Discuss why you would or would not prefer an essay-type question.

   _____

   _____

   _____

   _____

C. For a true-false question to be true, it must be totally true. You may be required to recognize a fact as being correct or incorrect, or to use reasoning to pronounce the statement true or false.

1. A statement that is partially true should be marked true.   T   F

D. Answers are provided on matching tests, but you must decide which item goes with which other item. Extra items may not match, or an item may be matchable to more than one other. Matching may be accomplished by drawing lines or writing the answer or its letter.

1. _____ true-false questions

   _____ essay questions

   _____ multiple choice questions

   _____ matching questions

   a. ask you to discuss an issue
   b. require you to match items
   c. give you possibilities
   d. do not allow for "maybe"

E. Sentence completion items ask you to supply a missing word or words anyplace in a sentence to make the statement correct. A word list may or may not be given.

1. Word choices may not be

   _____ in completion items.

Read and Apply

DIRECTIONS Read about some specific aspects of test taking.

There are several "tried and true" tips which help in taking tests, whether the questions are in objective or subjective form. Objective tests present questions in true-false, multiple choice, matching, sentence completion, or any combination of those forms. Subjective tests have one or more essay questions.

Objective questions are scored as either right or wrong. Unless directed otherwise, you should answer every question on an objective test. By doing so, you just may guess correctly when you're not sure of the correct answer. Occasionally, you may be advised not to answer objective items unless you're absolutely sure which answer is correct. In this case, there is a penalty for incorrect answers, and you are wise to not guess.

Essay questions require you to read a question, organize your thoughts in a meaningful way, and then write your answer. An answer on a subjective question may range anywhere from totally correct to totally incorrect. Points are generally given for each part of an answer that is correct, with a total score being compared to the total possible points.

Being alert to key words in test questions can be especially beneficial. Knowing that true-false questions must be totally correct to be marked "true," you'll want to be on the lookout for qualifying words such as "always," "never," "usually," or "only." Such a word can help you quickly identify the truth or untruth of a statement.

A good way to practice test-taking skills is to write and answer your own test questions, both subjective and objective. Who knows, one of your practice questions just might appear on the actual test! Look how well prepared you'd be!

DIRECTIONS Some tests require you to answer questions by making specific marks or coloring circles in designated places on the test or another paper. If tests are to be scored by computer, your marks must be inside the specified area. Think about what you've read about test-taking as you answer each group of questions by coloring in the corresponding numbered circle below.

1. A test is a way to check skills.   **a)** T   **b)** F

2. A test is always scored by a computer.   **a)** T   **b)** F

3. An essay is an example of an objective test.   **a)** T   **b)** F

4. You might be told not to answer every question.   **a)** T   **b)** F

5. A multiple choice question is an example of
   a. a subjective question.
   b. an objective question.
   c. both *a* and *b*.
   d. neither *a* nor *b*.

6. In a sentence completion question,
   a. you may have a word list of choices.
   b. you never have a word list of choices.
   c. you always have a word list of choices.
   d. none of the above.

7. To answer an essay question, you (a) may (b) may not give opinions.

8. There may be a _____ for guessing on objective tests.   **a)** essay

9. A true-false item may ask for _____.   **b)** reasoning

10. You would write a lot on an _____ question.   **c)** penalty

   d) matching

1. ⓐ ⓑ ⓒ ⓓ   6. ⓐ ⓑ ⓒ ⓓ
2. ⓐ ⓑ ⓒ ⓓ   7. ⓐ ⓑ ⓒ ⓓ
3. ⓐ ⓑ ⓒ ⓓ   8. ⓐ ⓑ ⓒ ⓓ
4. ⓐ ⓑ ⓒ ⓓ   9. ⓐ ⓑ ⓒ ⓓ
5. ⓐ ⓑ ⓒ ⓓ   10. ⓐ ⓑ ⓒ ⓓ

REMEMBER Test taking skills help you take tests.

Wanted: A Toothbrush

You obviously don't need to read every word of a phone book to find the phone number of your local pet store. You don't need to read every word of a reference book to answer a few questions. In this lesson, you'll learn about two methods of fast reading which help you find information you want. You'll also learn about what life might be like without a toothbrush.

 ## 1 KEYS to Skimming and Scanning

Some fast methods of reading give you quick information.

LEARN *Skimming* is reading fast to get the general idea and a few details. *Scanning* is a fast kind of reading for finding one or more specific facts. You'd skim a long letter if you haven't time to read all the news right now. When you need the answer to a particular question, you could skim the chapter, rather than read it entirely. You'd scan a map to find Arcadia, Wisconsin, or a schedule to find the time you have soccer practice.

DIRECTIONS Write *skim* or *scan* on the line to tell the best kind of reading for each reading purpose.

_____ **1.** Find out what TV channel a movie is on.

_____ **2.** Find an article for your report topic.

_____ **3.** Find two favorite jokes in a joke book.

_____ **4.** Find a word in the dictionary.

2 Practice Skimming and Scanning

DIRECTIONS When you scan for a specific fact, keep your mind on your reason for reading as you quickly move your eyes down the page. Read each question and keep it in mind as you scan the list of words. Write the answer on the line.

A. What word comes after the word *nourishment?*

_____

B. What word comes before the word *intermediate?*

_____

C. How many words begin with a vowel?

_____

D. Which word comes after the word that begins with *f?*

_____

1. intelligent
2. admirable
3. replenish
4. nourishment
5. entwined
6. imaginary
7. fluoride
8. meaningful
9. considerable
10. acquiring
11. hospitable
12. realistic
13. intermediate
14. paragraph
15. excellence
16. wonderful

DIRECTIONS Scan the TV listings to answer the questions.

	3	5	8	19	23	25	43	49	55
7 AM **7:30**	Today "	Good Morning America✔	Morning News The Morning	He-Man Defenders	Good Morning America✔	Human Behavior Health Issues	Tom and Jerry Bugs Bunny	Sesame Street✔	Consumer Zoobilee Zoo
8 AM **8:30**	" "	Morning Exchange	Program "	Heathcliff Silverhawks	" "	Faces of Culture Growing Years	Flintstones My Little Pony	Capt. Kangaroo Mister Rogers	Inspector Gadget Superfriends
9 AM **9:30**	AM Cleveland "	" "	Hour Magazine "	Bonanza "	Crook and Chase Morning Stretch	Joint Congressional	Barnaby Romper Room	Rainbow✔ Knowzone✔	90 and 9 Club "
10 AM **10:30**	Sale of Century Concentration	Donahue "	Pyramid Card Sharks	The 700 Club "	The 700 Club "	Iran/Contra Committee	Shopping Game Beaver	MotorWeek Louisiana Cookin'	A.M. Workout Marshal Dillon
11 AM **11:30**	Wheel of Fortune Scrabble	Who's Boss? Ryan's Hope	The Price Is Right	Richard Roberts "	Who's Boss? Bargain Hunters	Hearings or Local	Alice Andy Griffith	Austin City Limits	Family Affair Room for Daddy

A. A person who likes to start the day by catching up on the news would turn to which channel?

_____

B. What show would someone who likes cars watch at 10:00?

_____

C. It's 9:30 and you're tired of sitting still. What show would you watch to get some exercise?

_____

D. What time would you turn on channel 49 to learn some new recipes?

_____

3   Read and Apply

DIRECTIONS Read the first paragraph of the story slowly and carefully. Then read the reason-for-reading question before you skim the paragraph that follows. Write your answer on the lines.

Although you may sometimes wish there'd never been such an invention as the toothbrush, imagine not having anything to use to clean your teeth. A toothbrush, like many articles we use daily, is taken for granted as if it had always been available. In truth, people have not always had such a convenient device for oral hygiene. A look at life in another era just may give you a greater appreciation for the simple tool used so often without much thought.

Reason for Reading: How can you tell that the ancient Romans were intelligent, hardworking people?

Some of the roads, bridges, and aqueducts, which were built by the ancient Romans some two thousand years ago, still stand. These people who ruled the land around the Mediterranean Sea were especially concerned with health and cleanliness. For this and other reasons, they built elaborate bathing houses in every community. The baths were available to the public throughout the Roman empire. Although public baths encourage one aspect of personal hygiene, the Romans were without an effective means for good oral hygiene. They didn't have a simple tool we know as a toothbrush.

Answer: _____

_____

_____

_____

Read each reason for reading. Then skim the paragraph and complete the sentence.

Reason for Reading: Which early Romans spoke out on cleaning teeth?

A. The Romans had several among them who addressed the issue of teeth cleaning. One of these Roman citizens, Pliny the Elder, suggested that the teeth be cleaned with a piece of wool dipped in a mixture of honey and anise, the flavoring in licorice. This author of the first encyclopedia in the world wrote that the teeth could be cleaned by wrapping the moist wool around the index finger. Another writer, a poet called Ovid, claimed that women should clean their teeth in private if they wanted to make a good impression on others.

1. _____ and _____ talked about oral hygiene.

Reason for Reading: What did early Romans use to clean their teeth?

B. A "chew stick" was popular among early Romans. This was a wood piece which was splintered or shredded on the end. The splinters went between the teeth when the stick was chewed on. Toothpicks were also popular, with gold or silver toothpicks being a symbol of wealth. Toothpicks for the poor, however, were cut from wood or the bones of animals. Pliny advised the poor that bones of vultures should not be used to avoid getting bad breath.

1. Early Romans used

_____ or

_____ to clean their teeth.

Reason for Reading: What might toothbrushes have prevented?

C. The Romans had many dental problems for want of a toothbrush. Toothaches, loose teeth, gum disease, and lost teeth were prevalent. Celsus, a Roman doctor, suggested chewing unripe pears or apples or the use of a weak vinegar solution as a cure for gum disease. For a sore tooth, he recommended a hot sponge compress which was probably about as useless as Pliny's solution of touching a sore tooth with a lizard's bone when the moon was full.

1. The Romans may not have had

_____,

_____,

_____ and

_____ .

REMEMBER Scan or skim when you need pieces of information.

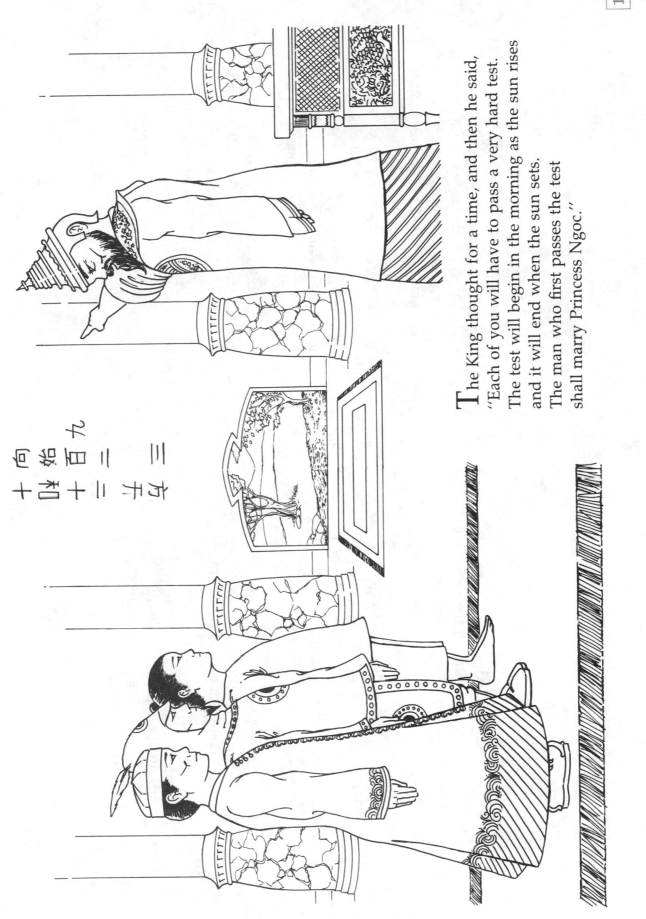

The King thought for a time, and then he said, "Each of you will have to pass a very hard test. The test will begin in the morning as the sun rises and it will end when the sun sets. The man who first passes the test shall marry Princess Ngoc."

三 万 九
三 三 日
百 十 和
十 十
向

The King said to them,
"Tell me why you think that you should marry the Princess."

The first man bowed low and said,
"Great King, I am a runner
and I can run faster than any other man
    in the land."

The second man bowed very low and said,
"Great King, I am an archer,
and I can fire a hundred arrows before
    you can wink an eye."

The third man bowed even lower and said,
"Mighty King, I am a poet,
and I can write more poems in one day
than any other man in the land."

He told the runner,
"You will run as fast as the wind
to the army camp on the far border of our land.
There you will see a drum,
with sides made of gold.
You will bring it back to me before the sun sets
if you wish to marry Princess Ngoc."

He told the archer,
"You will go to the great forest near the city
and you must shoot every leaf off every tree
before the sun sets,
if you wish to marry Princess Ngoc."

The King turned to the poet and said,
"You, poet, shall stay here in the palace.
We will give you paper and pens
and a room to work in.
You must write 100 times 100 poems
before the sun sets,
if you wish to marry Princess Ngoc."

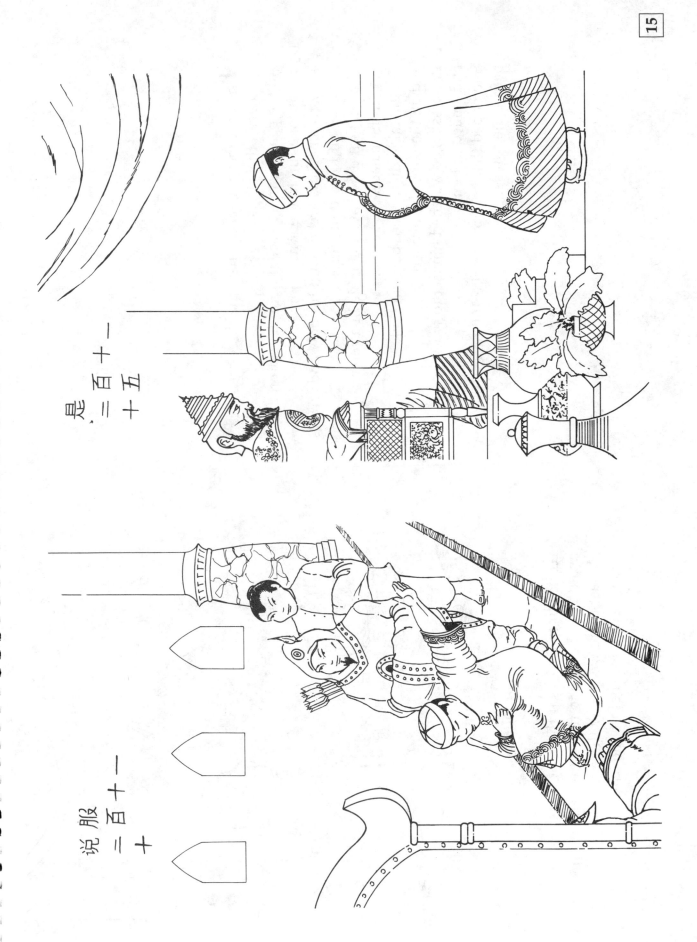

是
三百一
十五

说服
三百
十

The next morning at sunrise, the three men
began their tests.
All the people came to see the runner set off
on his long run to the army camp.
They watched the archer with his bow and arrows
as he set off toward the forest.
The poet sat down at a big table in a room
in the palace.
On the table there were pens and ink
and all the paper he needed.
Princess Ngoc watched him set to work
and smiled at him.
She hoped that he would write 100 times 100 poems
before the sun set.

只三男人左边

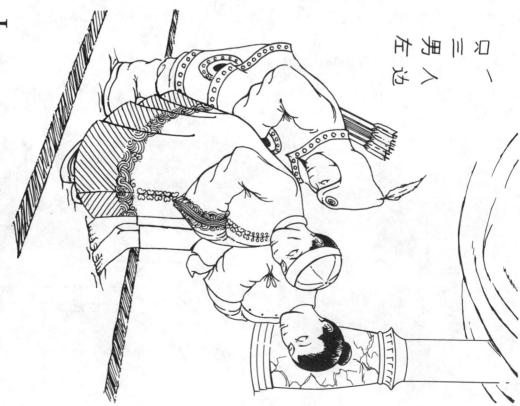

It began to look as if the King
would not be able to find a husband for his daughter.
At last there were only three men left.
They bowed low before the King.

竟　寞
開　始
二百十三
十七

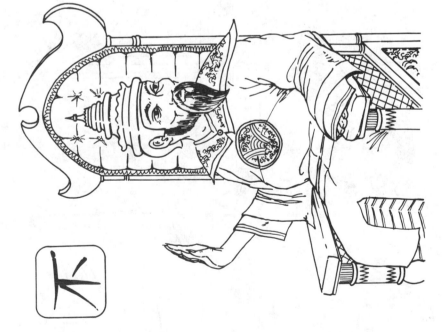

Time after time the King shook his head.
"That man is not the best.
Send him away.
That man is not the best.
Send him away."
One by one the men went sadly away,
not even seeing Princess Ngoc.

下

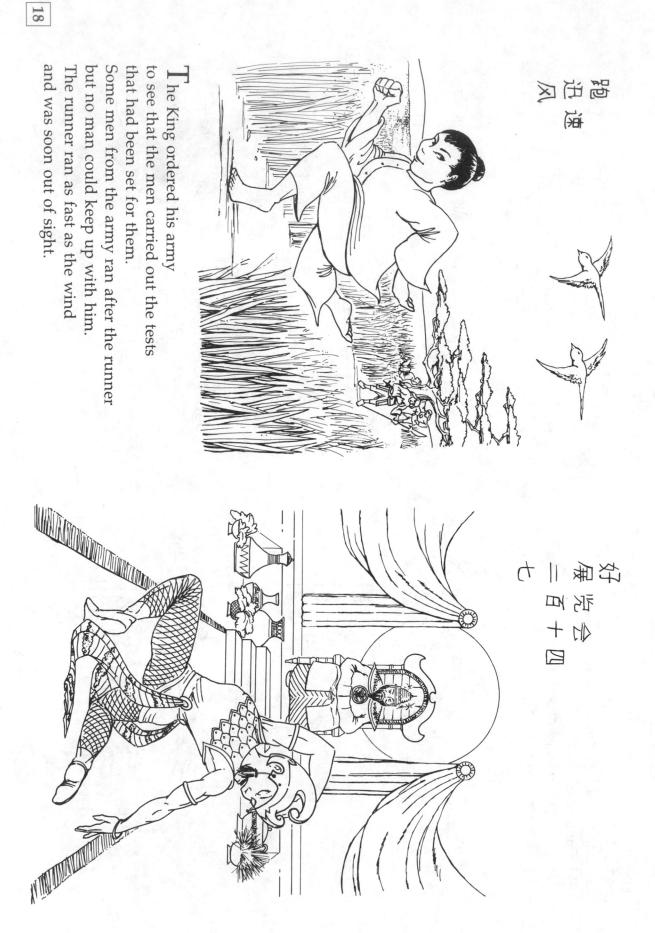

跑
迅
速

好
展
览
会
三
百
十
四
七

The King ordered his army
to see that the men carried out the tests
that had been set for them.
Some men from the army ran after the runner
but no man could keep up with him.
The runner ran as fast as the wind
and was soon out of sight.

The King watched them all.
All the dancers danced.
They danced the most beautiful dances.
All the painters painted.
They used colors which had never been
    seen before.
All the singers sang.
They sang some of the sweetest songs
that had ever been heard.
All the fighters fought.
Their swords flashed in the sun as they moved.
Each and every one of them tried his very best
because he wanted to marry the Princess.

The archer went to the forest
and fired his arrows at the leaves on the trees.
Soon he was up to his knees in the fallen leaves,
but there were still many leaves on the trees.
Then he was up to his neck in the fallen leaves,
but the more leaves he shot down,
the more leaves there seemed to be left on the trees.

The poet sat quietly at his table
and his pen filled sheet after sheet of paper
with poems.
Princess Ngoc sat in her garden and watched him.
She wished she knew how many poems
    he had written.
Time went by slowly.
Princess Ngoc wanted more than ever
to know how many poems the poet had written.
She left her garden
and went to the room where the poet sat at work.
When the poet saw the Princess he stopped work,
and bowed low to her.

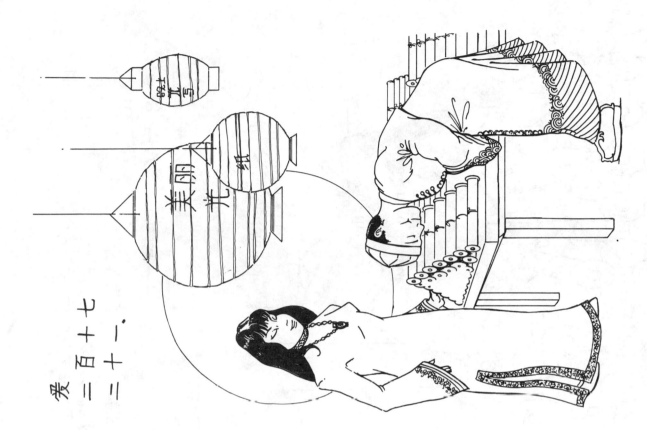

愛　美丽　光荣　教师

二百十七　三十一

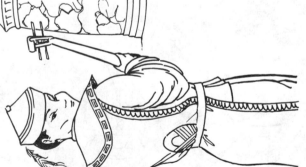

很
眼　业
男　性
市　民

Soon the city was full of men who all wanted to marry Princess Ngoc. There were dancers, singers, painters and fighters. Each of them said that he was the very best of all.

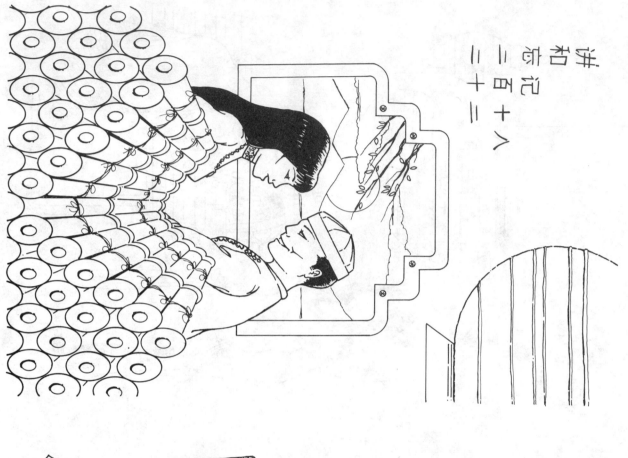

讲和
总记
二百十八
二十二

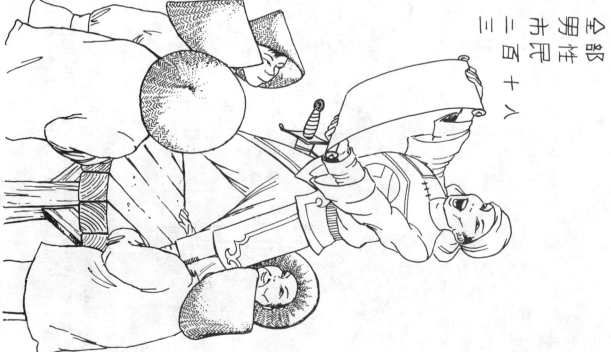

全部
男性市民
二百三
二百十八

When Princess Ngoc was old enough
    to be married
The King told her
that he would choose a husband for her.
In those days,
girls could not choose their own husbands.
Even a Princess had to do what her father told her.
"Your husband must be a good man,"
said the King.
"He must be very clever.
He must be the best man
in the land."

So the King sent his army out to tell all the people
that he was looking for a husband
    for Princess Ngoc.
The army went out across the land and told
all the men
that the King would choose
the cleverest and best man in the land
    to marry the Princess.

"How many poems have you written?"
asked Princess Ngoc.

"I have only one more poem to write," he told her.
"Then I will have passed the test the King
    has set for me."

Princess Ngoc was very happy when she heard this.
She liked the poet best of all
and was sure that he would make a very
    good husband.

They went on talking,
as they had so much to say to one another.
They forgot that the poet had not written
    his last poem,
and they forgot, too, about the archer
    and the runner.

A long time ago there lived a King
who ruled the land of Vietnam.
The King had only one child,
Princess Ngoc.
Her hair was as soft as black silk
and her smile was sweet and kind.
She grew up to be wise and good
and the King loved her very much.

金
殷
三百二十
二十四

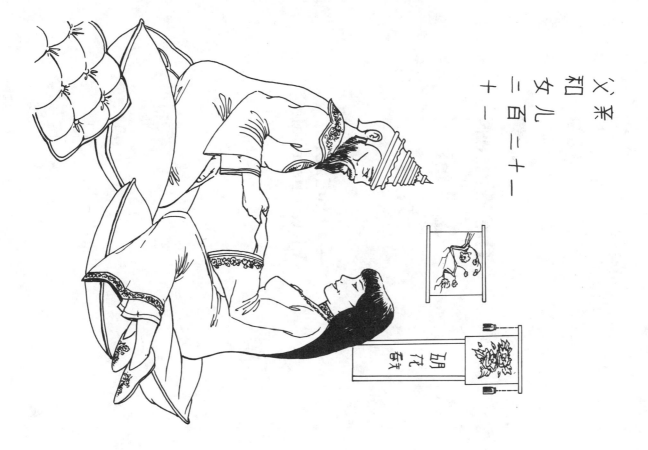

父親
和
女兒
三百二十一

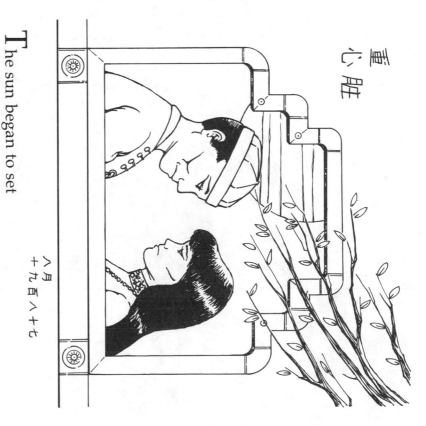

重
心
肝

八月
十九百八十七

The sun began to set
as Princess Ngoc and the poet talked.
Then they heard a loud banging noise.
It was the runner bringing the gold drum
    to the King.
The runner had won the test.
Princess Ngoc was very sad
for she knew now
that she could never marry the poet.

The Princess and the Poet

Poet

and the

—a traditional
Vietnamese tale